Activity Workbook
for
Understanding Linear Algebra

Activity Workbook
for
Understanding Linear Algebra

David Austin
Grand Valley State University

December 21, 2023

Edition: 2023 Update

Website: http://gvsu.edu/s/0Ck

[1]creativecommons.org

Preface

This workbook consists of the activities from *Understanding Linear Algebra*, which is available in a variety of formats at gvsu.edu/s/0Ck.

This workbook is meant to support students and instructors as a supplement to their use of the book. Each activity appears on its own page, and blank space is provided for students to work directly in the workbook. In this way, students can generate an organized and completed set of activities for future reference.

In addition, this workbook aims to develop readers' ability to reason about linear algebraic concepts and to apply that reasoning in a computational environment. In particular, Sage is introduced as a platform for performing many linear algebraic computations since it is freely available and its syntax mirrors common mathematical notation.

Readers may access Sage online using either the Sage cell server[2] or a provided page of Sage cells.[3]

Throughout the workbook, Sage cells appear in various places to encourage readers to use Sage to complete some relevant computation. These may appear with some pre-populated code, such as the one below, that you will want to copy into an online Sage cell.

```
A = matrix([[1,2], [2,1]])
```

Empty cells appear as shown below and are included to indicate part of an exercise or activity that is meant to be completed in Sage.

```

```

[2] sagecell.sagemath.org/
[3] https:gvsu.edu/s/0Ng

Contents

1 *Systems of equations*

1.1 What can we expect

Activity 1.1.1 In this activity, we consider sets of linear equations having just two unknowns. In this case, we can graph the solutions sets for the equations, which allows us to visualize different types of behavior.

a. On the grid below, graph the lines

$$y = x + 1$$
$$y = 2x - 1.$$

At what point or points (x, y), do the lines intersect? How many points (x, y) satisfy both equations?

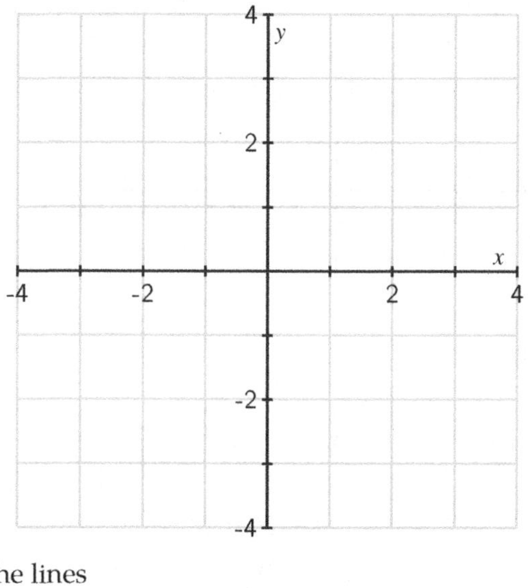

b. On the grid below, graph the lines

$$y = x + 1$$
$$y = x - 1.$$

At what point or points (x, y), do the lines intersect? How many points (x, y) satisfy both equations?

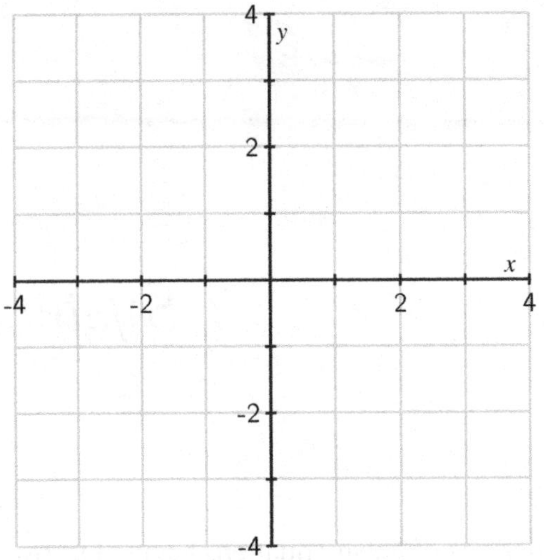

c. On the grid below, graph the line

$$y = x + 1.$$

How many points (x, y) satisfy this equation?

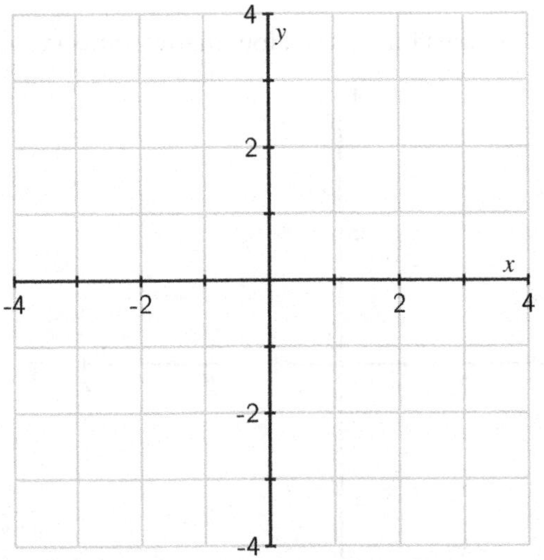

d. On the grid below, graph the lines

$$y = x + 1$$
$$y = 2x - 1$$
$$y = -x.$$

At what point or points (x, y), do the lines intersect? How many points (x, y) satisfy all three equations?

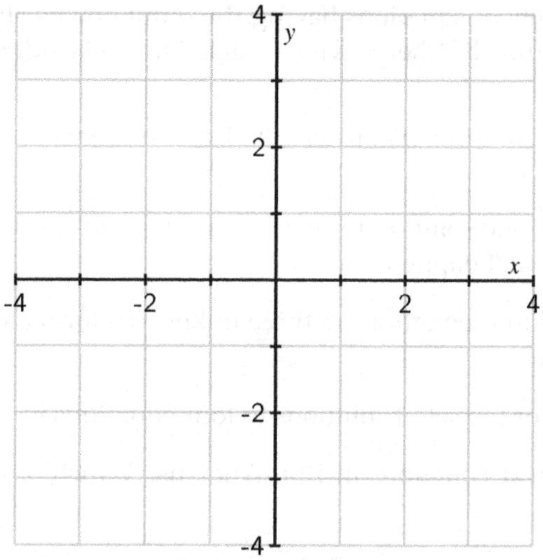

4
y
2
x
-4
-2
2
4
-2
-4

Activity 1.1.2 This activity considers sets of equations having three unknowns. In this case, we know that the solutions of a single equation form a plane. If it helps with visualization, consider using 3×5-inch index cards to represent planes.

a. Is it possible that there are no solutions to two linear equations in three unknowns? Either sketch an example or state a reason why it can't happen.

b. Is it possible that there is exactly one solution to two linear equations in three unknowns? Either sketch an example or state a reason why it can't happen.

c. Is it possible that the solutions to four equations in three unknowns form a line? Either sketch an example or state a reason why it can't happen.

d. What would you usually expect for the set of solutions to four equations in three unknowns?

e. Suppose we have a set of 500 linear equations in 10 unknowns. Which of the three possibilities would you expect to hold?

f. Suppose we have a set of 10 linear equations in 500 unknowns. Which of the three possibilities would you expect to hold?

Activity 1.1.3 Linear equations and their solutions.

a. Which of the following equations are linear? Please provide a justification for your response.

1. $$2x + xy - 3y^2 = 2.$$

2. $$-2x_1 + 3x_2 + 4x_3 - x_5 = 0.$$

3. $$x = 3z - 4y.$$

b. Consider the system of linear equations:

$$\begin{aligned} x + y \quad\; &= 3 \\ y - z &= 2 \\ 2x + y + z &= 4. \end{aligned}$$

1. Is $(x, y, z) = (1, 2, 0)$ a solution?
2. Is $(x, y, z) = (-2, 1, 0)$ a solution?
3. Is $(x, y, z) = (0, -3, 1)$ a solution?
4. Can you find a solution in which $y = 0$?
5. Do you think there are other solutions? Please explain your response.

1.2 Finding solutions to linear systems

Preview Activity 1.2.1 In this activity, we will consider some simple examples that will guide us in finding a more general approach.

a. Give a description of the solution space to the linear system:

$$\begin{aligned} x &= 2 \\ y &= -1. \end{aligned}$$

b. Give a description of the solution space to the linear system:

$$\begin{aligned} -x + 2y - z &= -3 \\ 3y + z &= -1 \\ 2z &= 4. \end{aligned}$$

c. Give a description of the solution space to the linear system:

$$\begin{aligned} x + 3y &= -1 \\ 2x + y &= 3. \end{aligned}$$

d. Describe the solution space to the linear equation $0x = 0$.

e. Describe the solution space to the linear equation $0x = 5$.

Activity 1.2.2 Gaussian Elimination. For each of the following linear systems, use Gaussian elimination to describe the solutions to the following systems of linear equations. In particular, determine whether each linear system has exactly one solution, infinitely many solutions, or no solutions.

a. $$\begin{aligned} x + y + 2z &= 1 \\ 2x - y - 2z &= 2 \\ -x + y + z &= 0 \end{aligned}$$

b. $$\begin{aligned} -x - 2y + 2z &= -1 \\ 2x + 4y - z &= 5 \\ x + 2y &= 3 \end{aligned}$$

c. $$\begin{aligned} -x - 2y + 2z &= -1 \\ 2x + 4y - z &= 5 \\ x + 2y &= 2 \end{aligned}$$

Activity 1.2.3 Augmented matrices and solution spaces.

a. Write the augmented matrix for the linear system

$$\begin{aligned} x + 2y - z &= 1 \\ 3x + 2y + 2z &= 7 \\ -x + 4z &= -3 \end{aligned}$$

and perform Gaussian elimination to describe the solution space in as much detail as you can.

b. Suppose that you have a linear system in the variables x and y whose augmented matrix is row equivalent to

$$\left[\begin{array}{cc|c} 1 & 0 & 3 \\ 0 & 1 & 0 \\ 0 & 0 & 0 \end{array}\right].$$

Write the linear system corresponding to this augmented matrix and describe its solution set in as much detail as you can.

c. Suppose that you have a linear system in the variables x and y whose augmented matrix is row equivalent to

$$\left[\begin{array}{cc|c} 1 & 0 & 3 \\ 0 & 1 & 0 \\ 0 & 0 & 1 \end{array}\right].$$

Write the linear system corresponding to this augmented matrix and describe its solution set in as much detail as you can.

d. Suppose that the augmented matrix of a linear system has the following shape where $*$ could be any real number.

$$\left[\begin{array}{ccccc|c} * & * & * & * & * & * \\ * & * & * & * & * & * \\ * & * & * & * & * & * \end{array}\right].$$

1. How many equations are there in this system and how many variables?
2. Based on our earlier discussion in Section 1.1, do you think it's possible that this system has exactly one solution, infinitely many solutions, or no solutions?
3. Suppose that this augmented matrix is row equivalent to

$$\left[\begin{array}{ccccc|c} 1 & 2 & 0 & 0 & 3 & 2 \\ 0 & 0 & 1 & 2 & -1 & -1 \\ 0 & 0 & 0 & 0 & 0 & 0 \end{array}\right].$$

Make a choice for the names of the variables and write the corresponding linear system. Does the system have exactly one solution, infinitely many solutions, or no solutions?

Activity 1.2.4 Identifying reduced row echelon matrices. Consider each of the following augmented matrices. Determine if the matrix is in reduced row echelon form. If it is not, perform a sequence of scaling, interchange, and replacement operations to obtain a row equivalent matrix that is in reduced row echelon form. Then use the reduced row echelon matrix to describe the solution space.

a. $\left[\begin{array}{ccc|c} 2 & 0 & 4 & -8 \\ 0 & 1 & 3 & 2 \end{array}\right]$.

b. $\left[\begin{array}{ccc|c} 1 & 0 & 0 & -1 \\ 0 & 1 & 0 & 3 \\ 0 & 0 & 1 & 1 \end{array}\right]$.

c. $\left[\begin{array}{ccc|c} 1 & 0 & 4 & 2 \\ 0 & 1 & 3 & 2 \\ 0 & 0 & 0 & 1 \end{array}\right]$.

d. $\left[\begin{array}{ccc|c} 0 & 1 & 3 & 2 \\ 0 & 0 & 0 & 0 \\ 1 & 0 & 4 & 2 \end{array}\right]$.

e. $\left[\begin{array}{ccc|c} 1 & 2 & -1 & 2 \\ 0 & 1 & -2 & 0 \\ 0 & 0 & 1 & 1 \end{array}\right]$.

1.3 Computation with Sage

Activity 1.3.1 Basic Sage commands.

a. Sage uses the standard operators +, -, *, /, and ^ for the usual arithmetic operations. By entering text in the cell below, ask Sage to evaluate

$$3 + 4(2^4 - 1)$$

```

```

b. Notice that we can create new lines by pressing *Enter* and entering additional commands on them. What happens when you evaluate this Sage cell?

```
5 * 3
10 - 4
```

Notice that we only see the result from the last command. With the `print` command, we may see earlier results, if we wish.

```
print(5 * 3)
print(10 - 4)
```

c. We may give a name to the result of one command and refer to it in a later command.

```
income = 1500 * 12
taxes = income * 0.15
print(taxes)
```

Suppose you have three tests in your linear algebra class and your scores are 90, 100, and 98. In the Sage cell below, add your scores together and call the result `total`. On the next line, find the average of your test scores and print it.

```

```

d. If you are not a programmer, you may ignore this part. If you are an experienced programmer, however, you should know that Sage is written in the Python programming language and that you may enter Python code into a Sage cell.

```
for i in range(10):
    print(i)
```

Activity 1.3.2 Using Sage to find row reduced echelon matrices.

a. Enter the following matrix into Sage.

$$\begin{bmatrix} -1 & -2 & 2 & -1 \\ 2 & 4 & -1 & 5 \\ 1 & 2 & 0 & 3 \end{bmatrix}$$

b. Give the matrix the name A by entering

```
A = matrix( ..., ..., [ ... ])
```

We may then find its reduced row echelon form by entering

```
A = matrix( ..., ..., [ ... ])
A.rref()
```

A common mistake is to forget the parentheses after `rref`.

Use Sage to find the reduced row echelon form of the matrix from Item a of this activity.

c. Use Sage to describe the solution space of the system of linear equations

$$\begin{aligned} -x_1 \qquad\qquad\quad + 2x_4 &= 4 \\ 3x_2 + x_3 + 2x_4 &= 3 \\ 4x_1 - 3x_2 \qquad\quad + x_4 &= 14 \\ 2x_2 + 2x_3 + x_4 &= 1 \end{aligned}$$

d. Consider the two matrices:

$$A = \begin{bmatrix} 1 & -2 & 1 & -3 \\ -2 & 4 & 1 & 1 \\ -4 & 8 & -1 & 7 \end{bmatrix}$$

$$B = \begin{bmatrix} 1 & -2 & 1 & -3 & 0 & 3 \\ -2 & 4 & 1 & 1 & 1 & -1 \\ -4 & 8 & -1 & 7 & 3 & 2 \end{bmatrix}$$

We say that B is an *augmentation* of A because it is obtained from A by adding some more columns.

Using Sage, define the matrices and compare their reduced row echelon forms. What do you notice about the relationship between the two reduced row echelon forms?

e. Using the system of equations in Item c, write the augmented matrix corresponding to the system of equations. What did you find for the reduced row echelon form of the augmented matrix?

Now write the coefficient matrix of this system of equations. What does Item d of this activity tell you about its reduced row echelon form?

1.4 Pivots and their influence on solution spaces

Preview Activity 1.4.1 Some basic observations about pivots.

a. Shown below is a matrix and its reduced row echelon form. Indicate the pivot positions.

$$\begin{bmatrix} 2 & 4 & 6 & -1 \\ -3 & 1 & 5 & 0 \\ 1 & 3 & 5 & 1 \end{bmatrix} \sim \begin{bmatrix} 1 & 0 & -1 & 0 \\ 0 & 1 & 2 & 0 \\ 0 & 0 & 0 & 1 \end{bmatrix}.$$

b. How many pivot positions can there be in one row? In a 3×5 matrix, what is the largest possible number of pivot positions? Give an example of a 3×5 matrix that has the largest possible number of pivot positions.

c. How many pivots can there be in one column? In a 5×3 matrix, what is the largest possible number of pivot positions? Give an example of a 5×3 matrix that has the largest possible number of pivot positions.

d. Give an example of a matrix with a pivot position in every row and every column. What is special about such a matrix?

Activity 1.4.2

a. Shown below are three augmented matrices in reduced row echelon form.

$$\left[\begin{array}{ccc|c} 1 & 0 & 0 & 3 \\ 0 & 1 & 0 & 0 \\ 0 & 0 & 1 & -2 \\ 0 & 0 & 0 & 0 \end{array}\right] \qquad \left[\begin{array}{ccc|c} 1 & 0 & 2 & 3 \\ 0 & 1 & -1 & 0 \\ 0 & 0 & 0 & 0 \\ 0 & 0 & 0 & 0 \end{array}\right] \qquad \left[\begin{array}{ccc|c} 1 & 0 & 2 & 0 \\ 0 & 1 & -1 & 0 \\ 0 & 0 & 0 & 1 \\ 0 & 0 & 0 & 0 \end{array}\right]$$

For each matrix, identify the pivot positions and determine if the corresponding linear system is consistent. Explain how the location of the pivots determines whether the system is consistent or inconsistent.

b. Each of the augmented matrices above has a row in which each entry is zero. What, if anything, does the presence of such a row tell us about the consistency of the corresponding linear system?

c. Give an example of a 3×5 augmented matrix in reduced row echelon form that represents a consistent system. Indicate the pivot positions in your matrix and explain why these pivot positions guarantee a consistent system.

d. Give an example of a 3×5 augmented matrix in reduced row echelon form that represents an inconsistent system. Indicate the pivot positions in your matrix and explain why these pivot positions guarantee an inconsistent system.

e. Write the reduced row echelon form of the coefficient matrix of the corresponding linear system in Item d? (Remember that the Augmentation Principle says that the reduced row echelon form of the coefficient matrix simply consists of the first four columns of the augmented matrix.) What do you notice about the pivot positions in this coefficient matrix?

f. Suppose we have a linear system for which the *coefficient* matrix has the following reduced row echelon form.

$$\begin{bmatrix} 1 & 0 & 0 & 0 & -1 \\ 0 & 1 & 0 & 0 & 2 \\ 0 & 0 & 1 & 0 & 0 \\ 0 & 0 & 0 & 1 & -3 \end{bmatrix}$$

What can you say about the consistency of the linear system?

Activity 1.4.3

a. Here are the three augmented matrices in reduced row echelon form that we considered in the previous section.

$$\left[\begin{array}{ccc|c} 1 & 0 & 0 & 3 \\ 0 & 1 & 0 & 0 \\ 0 & 0 & 1 & -2 \\ 0 & 0 & 0 & 0 \end{array}\right] \qquad \left[\begin{array}{ccc|c} 1 & 0 & 2 & 3 \\ 0 & 1 & -1 & 0 \\ 0 & 0 & 0 & 0 \\ 0 & 0 & 0 & 0 \end{array}\right] \qquad \left[\begin{array}{ccc|c} 1 & 0 & 2 & 0 \\ 0 & 1 & -1 & 0 \\ 0 & 0 & 0 & 1 \\ 0 & 0 & 0 & 0 \end{array}\right]$$

For each matrix, identify the pivot positions and state whether the corresponding linear system is consistent. If the system is consistent, explain whether the solution is unique or whether there are infinitely many solutions.

b. If possible, give an example of a 3×5 augmented matrix that corresponds to a linear system having a unique solution. If it is not possible, explain why.

c. If possible, give an example of a 5×3 augmented matrix that corresponds to a linear system having a unique solution. If it is not possible, explain why.

d. What condition on the pivot positions guarantees that a linear system has a unique solution?

e. If a linear system has a unique solution, what can we say about the relationship between the number of equations and the number of variables?

2 Vectors, matrices, and linear combinations

2.1 Vectors and linear combinations

Preview Activity 2.1.1 Scalar Multiplication and Vector Addition. Suppose that

$$\mathbf{v} = \begin{bmatrix} 3 \\ 1 \end{bmatrix}, \mathbf{w} = \begin{bmatrix} -1 \\ 2 \end{bmatrix}.$$

a. Find expressions for the vectors

$$\begin{array}{cccc} \mathbf{v}, & 2\mathbf{v}, & -\mathbf{v}, & -2\mathbf{v}, \\ \mathbf{w}, & 2\mathbf{w}, & -\mathbf{w}, & -2\mathbf{w}. \end{array}$$

and sketch them using Figure 2.1.2.

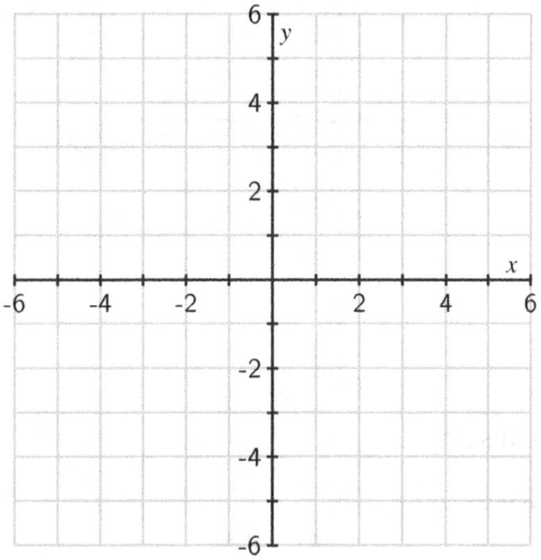

Figure 2.1.2 Sketch the vectors on this grid.

b. What geometric effect does scalar multiplication have on a vector? Also, describe the effect that multiplying by a negative scalar has.

c. Sketch the vectors $\mathbf{v}, \mathbf{w}, \mathbf{v} + \mathbf{w}$ using Figure 2.1.3.

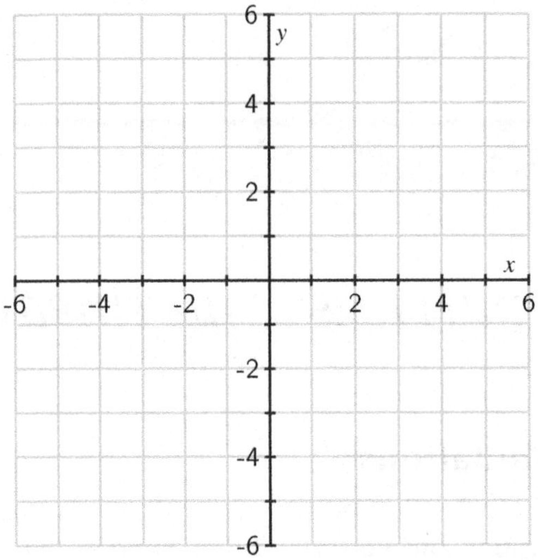

Figure 2.1.3 Sketch the vectors on this grid.

d. Consider vectors that have the form $\mathbf{v} + c\mathbf{w}$ where c is any scalar. Sketch a few of these vectors when, say, $c = -2, -1, 0, 1$, and 2. Give a geometric description of this set of vectors.

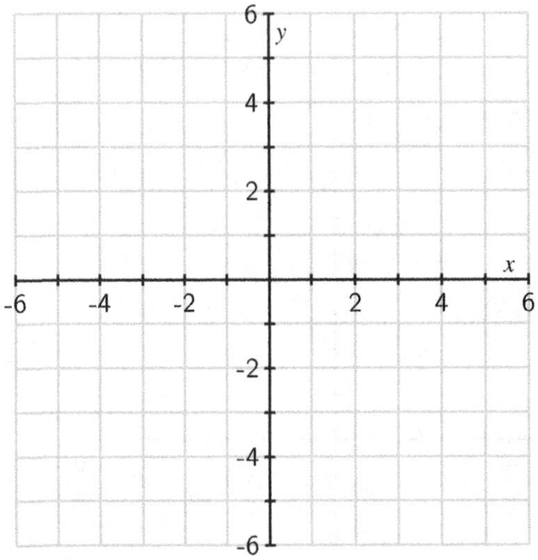

Figure 2.1.4 Sketch the vectors on this grid.

e. If c and d are two scalars, then the vector

$$c\mathbf{v} + d\mathbf{w}$$

is called a *linear combination* of the vectors **v** and **w**. Find the vector that is the linear combination when $c = -2$ and $d = 1$.

f. Can the vector $\begin{bmatrix} -31 \\ 37 \end{bmatrix}$ be represented as a linear combination of **v** and **w**? Asked differently, can we find scalars c and d such that $c\mathbf{v} + d\mathbf{w} = \begin{bmatrix} -31 \\ 37 \end{bmatrix}$.

Activity 2.1.2 In this activity, we will look at linear combinations of a pair of vectors, $\mathbf{v} = \begin{bmatrix} 2 \\ 1 \end{bmatrix}$ and $\mathbf{w} = \begin{bmatrix} 1 \\ 2 \end{bmatrix}$.

There is an interactive diagram, available at `gvsu.edu/s/0Je`, that accompanies this activity.

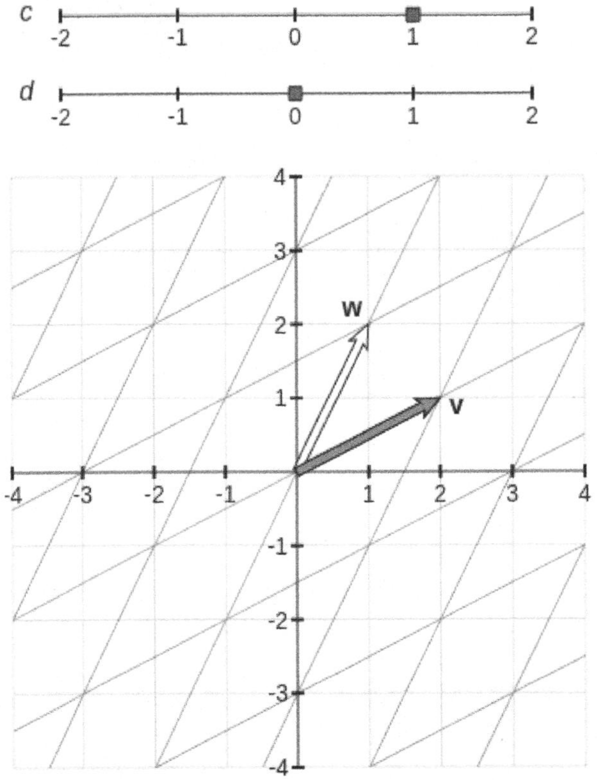

Figure 2.1.10 Linear combinations of vectors **v** and **w**.

a. The weight d is initially set to 0. Explain what happens as you vary c while keeping $d = 0$. How is this related to scalar multiplication?

b. What is the linear combination of **v** and **w** when $c = 1$ and $d = -2$? You may find this result using the diagram, but you should also verify it by computing the linear combination.

c. Describe the vectors that arise when the weight d is set to 1 and c is varied. How is this related to our investigations in the preview activity?

d. Can the vector $\begin{bmatrix} 0 \\ 0 \end{bmatrix}$ be expressed as a linear combination of **v** and **w**? If so, what are the weights c and d?

e. Can the vector $\begin{bmatrix} 3 \\ 0 \end{bmatrix}$ be expressed as a linear combination of **v** and **w**? If so, what are the weights c and d?

f. Verify the result from the previous part by algebraically finding the weights c and d that form the linear combination $\begin{bmatrix} 3 \\ 0 \end{bmatrix}$.

g. Can the vector $\begin{bmatrix} 1.3 \\ -1.7 \end{bmatrix}$ be expressed as a linear combination of **v** and **w**? What about the vector $\begin{bmatrix} 15.2 \\ 7.1 \end{bmatrix}$?

h. Are there any two-dimensional vectors that cannot be expressed as linear combinations of **v** and **w**?

Activity 2.1.3 Linear combinations and linear systems.

a. Given the vectors

$$\mathbf{v}_1 = \begin{bmatrix} 4 \\ 0 \\ 2 \\ 1 \end{bmatrix}, \mathbf{v}_2 = \begin{bmatrix} 1 \\ -3 \\ 3 \\ 1 \end{bmatrix}, \mathbf{v}_3 = \begin{bmatrix} -2 \\ 1 \\ 1 \\ 0 \end{bmatrix}, \mathbf{b} = \begin{bmatrix} 0 \\ 1 \\ 2 \\ -2 \end{bmatrix},$$

can $\mathbf{b}$ be expressed as a linear combination of $\mathbf{v}_1$, $\mathbf{v}_2$, and $\mathbf{v}_3$? Rephrase this question by writing a linear system for the weights c_1, c_2, and c_3 and use the Sage cell below to answer this question.

b. Consider the following linear system.

$$\begin{aligned} 3x_1 + 2x_2 - x_3 &= 4 \\ x_1 \qquad + 2x_3 &= 0 \\ -x_1 - x_2 + 3x_3 &= 1 \end{aligned}$$

Identify vectors $\mathbf{v}_1$, $\mathbf{v}_2$, $\mathbf{v}_3$, and $\mathbf{b}$ such that the question "Is this linear system consistent?" is equivalent to the question "Can $\mathbf{b}$ be expressed as a linear combination of $\mathbf{v}_1$, $\mathbf{v}_2$, and $\mathbf{v}_3$?"

c. Consider the vectors

$$\mathbf{v}_1 = \begin{bmatrix} 0 \\ -2 \\ 1 \end{bmatrix}, \mathbf{v}_2 = \begin{bmatrix} 1 \\ 1 \\ -1 \end{bmatrix}, \mathbf{v}_3 = \begin{bmatrix} 2 \\ 0 \\ -1 \end{bmatrix}, \mathbf{b} = \begin{bmatrix} -1 \\ 3 \\ -1 \end{bmatrix}.$$

Can $\mathbf{b}$ be expressed as a linear combination of $\mathbf{v}_1$, $\mathbf{v}_2$, and $\mathbf{v}_3$? If so, can $\mathbf{b}$ be written as a linear combination of these vectors in more than one way?

d. Considering the vectors $\mathbf{v}_1$, $\mathbf{v}_2$, and $\mathbf{v}_3$ from the previous part, can we write every three-dimensional vector $\mathbf{b}$ as a linear combination of these vectors? Explain how the pivot positions of the matrix $\begin{bmatrix} \mathbf{v}_1 & \mathbf{v}_2 & \mathbf{v}_3 \end{bmatrix}$ help answer this question.

e. Now consider the vectors

$$\mathbf{v}_1 = \begin{bmatrix} 0 \\ -2 \\ 1 \end{bmatrix}, \mathbf{v}_2 = \begin{bmatrix} 1 \\ 1 \\ -1 \end{bmatrix}, \mathbf{v}_3 = \begin{bmatrix} 1 \\ -1 \\ -2 \end{bmatrix}, \mathbf{b} = \begin{bmatrix} 0 \\ 8 \\ -4 \end{bmatrix}.$$

Can $\mathbf{b}$ be expressed as a linear combination of $\mathbf{v}_1$, $\mathbf{v}_2$, and $\mathbf{v}_3$? If so, can $\mathbf{b}$ be written as a linear combination of these vectors in more than one way?

f. Considering the vectors $\mathbf{v}_1$, $\mathbf{v}_2$, and $\mathbf{v}_3$ from the previous part, can we write every three-dimensional vector $\mathbf{b}$ as a linear combination of these vectors? Explain how the pivot positions of the matrix $\begin{bmatrix} \mathbf{v}_1 & \mathbf{v}_2 & \mathbf{v}_3 \end{bmatrix}$ help answer this question.

2.2 Matrix multiplication and linear combinations

Preview Activity 2.2.1 Matrix operations.

a. Compute the scalar multiple

$$-3\begin{bmatrix} 3 & 1 & 0 \\ -4 & 3 & -1 \end{bmatrix}.$$

b. Find the sum

$$\begin{bmatrix} 0 & -3 \\ 1 & -2 \\ 3 & 4 \end{bmatrix} + \begin{bmatrix} 4 & -1 \\ -2 & 2 \\ 1 & 1 \end{bmatrix}.$$

c. Suppose that A and B are two matrices. What do we need to know about their shapes before we can form the sum $A + B$?

d. The matrix I_n, which we call the *identity* matrix, is the $n \times n$ matrix whose entries are zero except for the diagonal entries, all of which are 1. For instance,

$$I_3 = \begin{bmatrix} 1 & 0 & 0 \\ 0 & 1 & 0 \\ 0 & 0 & 1 \end{bmatrix}.$$

If we can form the sum $A + I_n$, what must be true about the matrix A?

e. Find the matrix $A - 2I_3$ where

$$A = \begin{bmatrix} 1 & 2 & -2 \\ 2 & -3 & 3 \\ -2 & 3 & 4 \end{bmatrix}.$$

Activity 2.2.2 Matrix-vector multiplication.

a. Find the matrix product

$$\begin{bmatrix} 1 & 2 & 0 & -1 \\ 2 & 4 & -3 & -2 \\ -1 & -2 & 6 & 1 \end{bmatrix} \begin{bmatrix} 3 \\ 1 \\ -1 \\ 1 \end{bmatrix}.$$

b. Suppose that A is the matrix

$$\begin{bmatrix} 3 & -1 & 0 \\ 0 & -2 & 4 \\ 2 & 1 & 5 \\ 1 & 0 & 3 \end{bmatrix}.$$

If $A\mathbf{x}$ is defined, what is the dimension of the vector $\mathbf{x}$ and what is the dimension of $A\mathbf{x}$?

c. A vector whose entries are all zero is denoted by $\mathbf{0}$. If A is a matrix, what is the product $A\mathbf{0}$?

d. Suppose that $I = \begin{bmatrix} 1 & 0 & 0 \\ 0 & 1 & 0 \\ 0 & 0 & 1 \end{bmatrix}$ is the identity matrix and $\mathbf{x} = \begin{bmatrix} x_1 \\ x_2 \\ x_3 \end{bmatrix}$. Find the product $I\mathbf{x}$ and explain why I is called the identity matrix.

e. Suppose we write the matrix A in terms of its columns as

$$A = \begin{bmatrix} \mathbf{v}_1 & \mathbf{v}_2 & \cdots & \mathbf{v}_n \end{bmatrix}.$$

If the vector $\mathbf{e}_1 = \begin{bmatrix} 1 \\ 0 \\ \vdots \\ 0 \end{bmatrix}$, what is the product $A\mathbf{e}_1$?

f. Suppose that

$$A = \begin{bmatrix} 1 & 2 \\ -1 & 1 \end{bmatrix}, \mathbf{b} = \begin{bmatrix} 6 \\ 0 \end{bmatrix}.$$

Is there a vector $\mathbf{x}$ such that $A\mathbf{x} = \mathbf{b}$?

Activity 2.2.3 Sage can find the product of a matrix and vector using the * operator. For example,

```
A = matrix(2,2,[1,2,2,1])
v = vector([3,-1])
A*v
```

a. Use Sage to evaluate the product

$$\begin{bmatrix} 1 & 2 & 0 & -1 \\ 2 & 4 & -3 & -2 \\ -1 & -2 & 6 & 1 \end{bmatrix} \begin{bmatrix} 3 \\ 1 \\ -1 \\ 1 \end{bmatrix}$$

from Item a of the previous activity.

b. In Sage, define the matrix and vectors

$$A = \begin{bmatrix} -2 & 0 \\ 3 & 1 \\ 4 & 2 \end{bmatrix}, \mathbf{0} = \begin{bmatrix} 0 \\ 0 \end{bmatrix}, \mathbf{v} = \begin{bmatrix} -2 \\ 3 \end{bmatrix}, \mathbf{w} = \begin{bmatrix} 1 \\ 2 \end{bmatrix}.$$

c. What do you find when you evaluate $A\mathbf{0}$?

d. What do you find when you evaluate $A(3\mathbf{v})$ and $3(A\mathbf{v})$ and compare your results?

e. What do you find when you evaluate $A(\mathbf{v} + \mathbf{w})$ and $A\mathbf{v} + A\mathbf{w}$ and compare your results?

Activity 2.2.4 The equation $A\mathbf{x} = \mathbf{b}$.

a. Consider the linear system

$$\begin{aligned} 2x + y - 3z &= 4 \\ -x + 2y + z &= 3 \\ 3x - y &= -4. \end{aligned}$$

Identify the matrix A and vector $\mathbf{b}$ to express this system in the form $A\mathbf{x} = \mathbf{b}$.

b. If A and $\mathbf{b}$ are as below, write the linear system corresponding to the equation $A\mathbf{x} = \mathbf{b}$ and describe its solution space, using a parametric description if appropriate:

$$A = \begin{bmatrix} 3 & -1 & 0 \\ -2 & 0 & 6 \end{bmatrix}, \quad \mathbf{b} = \begin{bmatrix} -6 \\ 2 \end{bmatrix}.$$

c. Describe the solution space of the equation

$$\begin{bmatrix} 1 & 2 & 0 & -1 \\ 2 & 4 & -3 & -2 \\ -1 & -2 & 6 & 1 \end{bmatrix} \mathbf{x} = \begin{bmatrix} -1 \\ 1 \\ 5 \end{bmatrix}.$$

d. Suppose A is an $m \times n$ matrix. What can you guarantee about the solution space of the equation $A\mathbf{x} = \mathbf{0}$?

Activity 2.2.5 Consider the matrices

$$A = \begin{bmatrix} 1 & 3 & 2 \\ -3 & 4 & -1 \end{bmatrix}, \quad B = \begin{bmatrix} 3 & 0 \\ 1 & 2 \\ -2 & -1 \end{bmatrix}.$$

a. Before computing, first explain why the shapes of A and B enable us to form the product AB. Then describe the shape of AB.

b. Compute the product AB.

c. Sage can multiply matrices using the $*$ operator. Define the matrices A and B in the Sage cell below and check your work by computing AB.

d. Are we able to form the matrix product BA? If so, use the Sage cell above to find BA. Is it generally true that $AB = BA$?

e. Suppose we form the three matrices.

$$A = \begin{bmatrix} 1 & 2 \\ 3 & -2 \end{bmatrix}, B = \begin{bmatrix} 0 & 4 \\ 2 & -1 \end{bmatrix}, C = \begin{bmatrix} -1 & 3 \\ 4 & 3 \end{bmatrix}.$$

Compare what happens when you compute $A(B + C)$ and $AB + AC$. State your finding as a general principle.

f. Compare the results of evaluating $A(BC)$ and $(AB)C$ and state your finding as a general principle.

g. When we are dealing with real numbers, we know if $a \neq 0$ and $ab = ac$, then $b = c$. Define matrices

$$A = \begin{bmatrix} 1 & 2 \\ -2 & -4 \end{bmatrix}, B = \begin{bmatrix} 3 & 0 \\ 1 & 3 \end{bmatrix}, C = \begin{bmatrix} 1 & 2 \\ 2 & 2 \end{bmatrix}$$

and compute AB and AC.

If $AB = AC$, is it necessarily true that $B = C$?

h. Again, with real numbers, we know that if $ab = 0$, then either $a = 0$ or $b = 0$. Define

$$A = \begin{bmatrix} 1 & 2 \\ -2 & -4 \end{bmatrix}, B = \begin{bmatrix} 2 & -4 \\ -1 & 2 \end{bmatrix}$$

and compute AB.

If $AB = 0$, is it necessarily true that either $A = 0$ or $B = 0$?

2.3 The span of a set of vectors

Preview Activity 2.3.1 The existence of solutions.

a. If the equation $A\mathbf{x} = \mathbf{b}$ is inconsistent, what can we say about the pivot positions of the augmented matrix $\left[\begin{array}{c|c} A & \mathbf{b} \end{array}\right]$?

b. Consider the matrix A

$$A = \begin{bmatrix} 1 & 0 & -2 \\ -2 & 2 & 2 \\ 1 & 1 & -3 \end{bmatrix}.$$

If $\mathbf{b} = \begin{bmatrix} 2 \\ 2 \\ 5 \end{bmatrix}$, is the equation $A\mathbf{x} = \mathbf{b}$ consistent? If so, find a solution.

c. If $\mathbf{b} = \begin{bmatrix} 2 \\ 2 \\ 6 \end{bmatrix}$, is the equation $A\mathbf{x} = \mathbf{b}$ consistent? If so, find a solution.

d. Identify the pivot positions of A.

e. For our two choices of the vector $\mathbf{b}$, one equation $A\mathbf{x} = \mathbf{b}$ has a solution and the other does not. What feature of the pivot positions of the matrix A tells us to expect this?

Activity 2.3.2 Let's look at two examples to develop some intuition for the concept of span.

a. First, we will consider the set of vectors

$$\mathbf{v} = \begin{bmatrix} 1 \\ 2 \end{bmatrix}, \quad \mathbf{w} = \begin{bmatrix} -2 \\ -4 \end{bmatrix}.$$

There is an interactive diagram, available at `gvsu.edu/s/0Jg`, that accompanies this activity. The diagram at the top of that page accompanies part a of this activity.

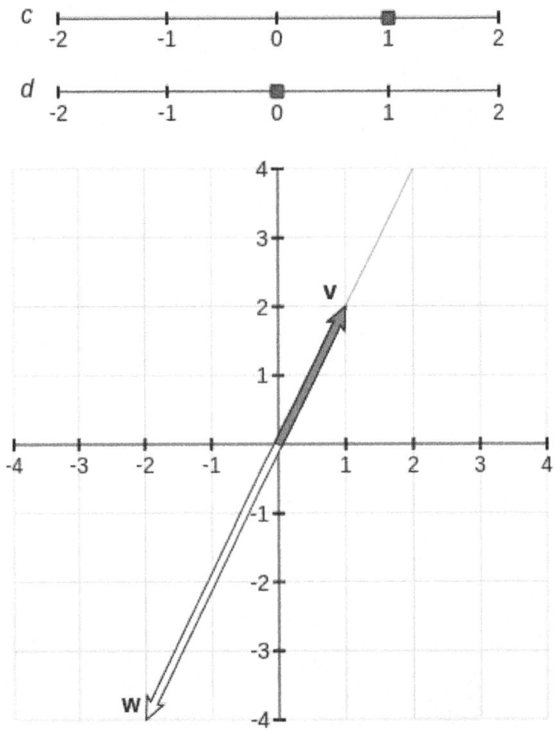

Figure 2.3.3 An interactive diagram for constructing linear combinations of the vectors **v** and **w**.

1. What vector is the linear combination of **v** and **w** with weights:
   - $c = 2$ and $d = 0$?
   - $c = 1$ and $d = 1$?
   - $c = 0$ and $d = -1$?
2. Can the vector $\begin{bmatrix} 2 \\ 4 \end{bmatrix}$ be expressed as a linear combination of **v** and **w**? Is the vector $\begin{bmatrix} 2 \\ 4 \end{bmatrix}$ in the span of **v** and **w**?
3. Can the vector $\begin{bmatrix} 3 \\ 0 \end{bmatrix}$ be expressed as a linear combination of **v** and **w**? Is the vector $\begin{bmatrix} 3 \\ 0 \end{bmatrix}$ in the span of **v** and **w**?
4. Describe the set of vectors in the span of **v** and **w**.
5. For what vectors **b** does the equation

$$\begin{bmatrix} 1 & -2 \\ 2 & -4 \end{bmatrix} \mathbf{x} = \mathbf{b}$$

   have a solution?

b. We will now look at an example where

$$\mathbf{v} = \begin{bmatrix} 2 \\ 1 \end{bmatrix}, \quad \mathbf{w} = \begin{bmatrix} 1 \\ 2 \end{bmatrix}.$$

The diagram at the bottom of the page at `gvsu.edu/s/0Jg` accompanies part b of this activity.

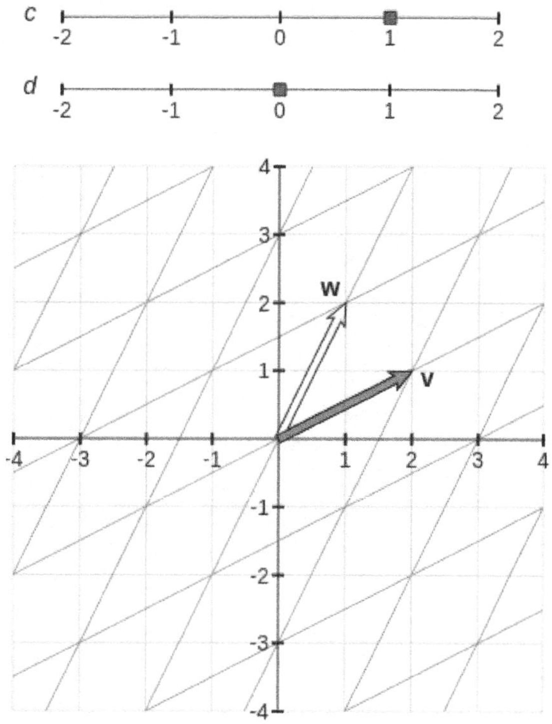

Figure 2.3.4 An interactive diagram for constructing linear combinations of the vectors **v** and **w**.

1. What vector is the linear combination of **v** and **w** with weights:
   - $c = 2$ and $d = 0$?
   - $c = 1$ and $d = 1$?
   - $c = 0$ and $d = -1$?
2. Can the vector $\begin{bmatrix} -2 \\ 2 \end{bmatrix}$ be expressed as a linear combination of **v** and **w**? Is the vector $\begin{bmatrix} -2 \\ 2 \end{bmatrix}$ in the span of **v** and **w**?
3. Can the vector $\begin{bmatrix} 3 \\ 0 \end{bmatrix}$ be expressed as a linear combination of **v** and **w**? Is the vector $\begin{bmatrix} 3 \\ 0 \end{bmatrix}$ in the span of **v** and **w**?
4. Describe the set of vectors in the span of **v** and **w**.
5. For what vectors **b** does the equation

$$\begin{bmatrix} 2 & 1 \\ 1 & 2 \end{bmatrix} \mathbf{x} = \mathbf{b}$$

   have a solution?

Activity 2.3.3 In this activity, we will look at the span of sets of vectors in $\mathbb{R}^3$.

a. Suppose $\mathbf{v} = \begin{bmatrix} 1 \\ 2 \\ 1 \end{bmatrix}$. Give a geometric description of Span$\{\mathbf{v}\}$ and a rough sketch of $\mathbf{v}$ and its span in Figure 2.3.10.

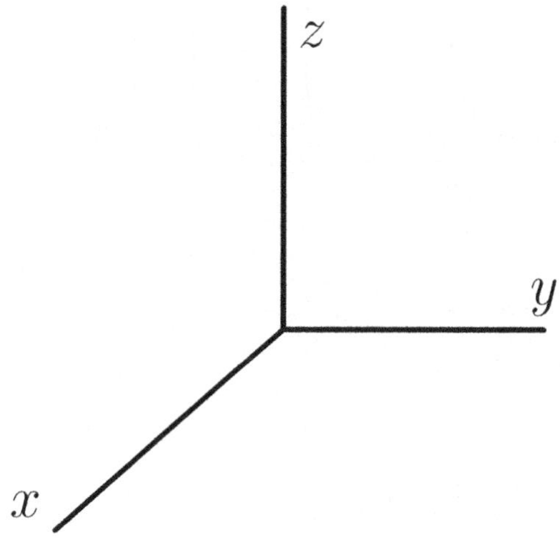

Figure 2.3.10 A three-dimensional coordinate system for sketching $\mathbf{v}$ and its span.

b. Now consider the two vectors

$$\mathbf{e}_1 = \begin{bmatrix} 1 \\ 0 \\ 0 \end{bmatrix}, \quad \mathbf{e}_2 = \begin{bmatrix} 0 \\ 1 \\ 0 \end{bmatrix}.$$

Sketch the vectors below. Then give a geometric description of Span$\{\mathbf{e}_1, \mathbf{e}_2\}$ and a rough sketch of the span in Figure 2.3.11.

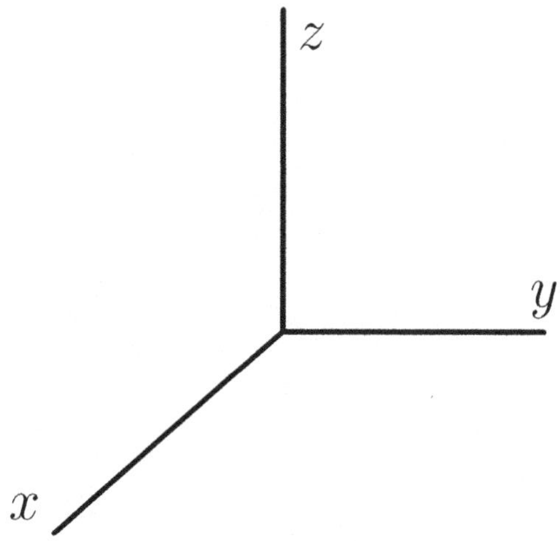

Figure 2.3.11 A coordinate system for sketching $\mathbf{e}_1$, $\mathbf{e}_2$, and Span$\{\mathbf{e}_1, \mathbf{e}_2\}$.

c. Let's now look at this situation algebraically by writing write $\mathbf{b} = \begin{bmatrix} b_1 \\ b_2 \\ b_3 \end{bmatrix}$. Determine the conditions on b_1, b_2, and b_3 so that $\mathbf{b}$ is in Span$\{\mathbf{e}_1, \mathbf{e}_2\}$ by considering the linear system

$$\begin{bmatrix} \mathbf{e}_1 & \mathbf{e}_2 \end{bmatrix} \mathbf{x} = \mathbf{b}$$

or

$$\begin{bmatrix} 1 & 0 \\ 0 & 1 \\ 0 & 0 \end{bmatrix} \mathbf{x} = \begin{bmatrix} b_1 \\ b_2 \\ b_3 \end{bmatrix}.$$

Explain how this relates to your sketch of Span$\{\mathbf{e}_1, \mathbf{e}_2\}$.

d. Consider the vectors

$$\mathbf{v}_1 = \begin{bmatrix} 1 \\ 1 \\ -1 \end{bmatrix}, \quad \mathbf{v}_2 = \begin{bmatrix} 0 \\ 2 \\ 1 \end{bmatrix}.$$

1. Is the vector $\mathbf{b} = \begin{bmatrix} 1 \\ -2 \\ 4 \end{bmatrix}$ in Span$\{\mathbf{v}_1, \mathbf{v}_2\}$?

2. Is the vector $\mathbf{b} = \begin{bmatrix} -2 \\ 0 \\ 3 \end{bmatrix}$ in Span$\{\mathbf{v}_1, \mathbf{v}_2\}$?

3. Give a geometric description of Span$\{\mathbf{v}_1, \mathbf{v}_2\}$.

e. Consider the vectors

$$\mathbf{v}_1 = \begin{bmatrix} 1 \\ 1 \\ -1 \end{bmatrix}, \mathbf{v}_2 = \begin{bmatrix} 0 \\ 2 \\ 1 \end{bmatrix}, \mathbf{v}_3 = \begin{bmatrix} 1 \\ -2 \\ 4 \end{bmatrix}.$$

Form the matrix $\begin{bmatrix} \mathbf{v}_1 & \mathbf{v}_2 & \mathbf{v}_3 \end{bmatrix}$ and find its reduced row echelon form.

What does this tell you about Span$\{\mathbf{v}_1, \mathbf{v}_2, \mathbf{v}_3\}$?

f. If the span of a set of vectors $\mathbf{v}_1, \mathbf{v}_2, \ldots, \mathbf{v}_n$ is $\mathbb{R}^3$, what can you say about the pivot positions of the matrix $\begin{bmatrix} \mathbf{v}_1 & \mathbf{v}_2 & \ldots & \mathbf{v}_n \end{bmatrix}$?

g. What is the smallest number of vectors such that Span$\{\mathbf{v}_1, \mathbf{v}_2, \ldots, \mathbf{v}_n\} = \mathbb{R}^3$?

2.4 Linear independence

Preview Activity 2.4.1 Let's begin by looking at some sets of vectors in $\mathbb{R}^3$. As we saw in the previous section, the span of a set of vectors in $\mathbb{R}^3$ will be either a line, a plane, or $\mathbb{R}^3$ itself.

a. Consider the following vectors in $\mathbb{R}^3$:

$$\mathbf{v}_1 = \begin{bmatrix} 0 \\ -1 \\ 2 \end{bmatrix}, \mathbf{v}_2 = \begin{bmatrix} 3 \\ 1 \\ -1 \end{bmatrix}, \mathbf{v}_3 = \begin{bmatrix} 2 \\ 0 \\ 1 \end{bmatrix}.$$

Describe the span of these vectors, $\text{Span}\{\mathbf{v}_1, \mathbf{v}_2, \mathbf{v}_3\}$, as a line, a plane, or $\mathbb{R}^3$.

b. Now consider the set of vectors:

$$\mathbf{w}_1 = \begin{bmatrix} 0 \\ -1 \\ 2 \end{bmatrix}, \mathbf{w}_2 = \begin{bmatrix} 3 \\ 1 \\ -1 \end{bmatrix}, \mathbf{w}_3 = \begin{bmatrix} 3 \\ 0 \\ 1 \end{bmatrix}.$$

Describe the span of these vectors, $\text{Span}\{\mathbf{w}_1, \mathbf{w}_2, \mathbf{w}_3\}$, as a line, a plane, or $\mathbb{R}^3$.

c. Show that the vector $\mathbf{w}_3$ is a linear combination of $\mathbf{w}_1$ and $\mathbf{w}_2$ by finding weights such that

$$\mathbf{w}_3 = c\mathbf{w}_1 + d\mathbf{w}_2.$$

d. Explain why any linear combination of $\mathbf{w}_1$, $\mathbf{w}_2$, and $\mathbf{w}_3$,

$$c_1\mathbf{w}_1 + c_2\mathbf{w}_2 + c_3\mathbf{w}_3$$

can be written as a linear combination of $\mathbf{w}_1$ and $\mathbf{w}_2$.

e. Explain why

$$\text{Span}\{\mathbf{w}_1, \mathbf{w}_2, \mathbf{w}_3\} = \text{Span}\{\mathbf{w}_1, \mathbf{w}_2\}.$$

Activity 2.4.2 We would like to develop a means to detect when a set of vectors is linearly dependent. This activity will point the way.

a. Suppose we have five vectors in $\mathbb{R}^4$ that form the columns of a matrix having reduced row echelon form

$$\begin{bmatrix} \mathbf{v}_1 & \mathbf{v}_2 & \mathbf{v}_3 & \mathbf{v}_4 & \mathbf{v}_5 \end{bmatrix} \sim \begin{bmatrix} 1 & 0 & -1 & 0 & 2 \\ 0 & 1 & 2 & 0 & 3 \\ 0 & 0 & 0 & 1 & -1 \\ 0 & 0 & 0 & 0 & 0 \end{bmatrix}.$$

Is it possible to write one of the vectors $\mathbf{v}_1, \mathbf{v}_2, \ldots, \mathbf{v}_5$ as a linear combination of the others? If so, show explicitly how one vector appears as a linear combination of some of the other vectors. Is this set of vectors linearly dependent or independent?

b. Suppose we have another set of three vectors in $\mathbb{R}^4$ that form the columns of a matrix having reduced row echelon form

$$\begin{bmatrix} \mathbf{w}_1 & \mathbf{w}_2 & \mathbf{w}_3 \end{bmatrix} \sim \begin{bmatrix} 1 & 0 & 0 \\ 0 & 1 & 0 \\ 0 & 0 & 1 \\ 0 & 0 & 0 \end{bmatrix}.$$

Is it possible to write one of these vectors $\mathbf{w}_1, \mathbf{w}_2, \mathbf{w}_3$ as a linear combination of the others? If so, show explicitly how one vector appears as a linear combination of some of the other vectors. Is this set of vectors linearly dependent or independent?

c. By looking at the pivot positions, how can you determine whether the columns of a matrix are linearly dependent or independent?

d. If one vector in a set is the zero vector $\mathbf{0}$, can the set of vectors be linearly independent?

e. Suppose a set of vectors in $\mathbb{R}^{10}$ has twelve vectors. Is it possible for this set to be linearly independent?

Activity 2.4.3 Linear independence and homogeneous equations.

a. Explain why the homogeneous equation $A\mathbf{x} = \mathbf{0}$ is consistent no matter the matrix A.

b. Consider the matrix

$$A = \begin{bmatrix} 3 & 2 & 0 \\ -1 & 0 & -2 \\ 2 & 1 & 1 \end{bmatrix}$$

whose columns we denote by $\mathbf{v}_1$, $\mathbf{v}_2$, and $\mathbf{v}_3$. Describe the solution space of the homogeneous equation $A\mathbf{x} = \mathbf{0}$ using a parametric description, if appropriate.

c. Find a nonzero solution to the homogeneous equation and use it to find weights c_1, c_2, and c_3 such that

$$c_1\mathbf{v}_1 + c_2\mathbf{v}_2 + c_3\mathbf{v}_3 = \mathbf{0}.$$

d. Use the equation you found in the previous part to write one of the vectors as a linear combination of the others.

e. Are the vectors $\mathbf{v}_1$, $\mathbf{v}_2$, and $\mathbf{v}_3$ linearly dependent or independent?

2.5 Matrix transformations

Preview Activity 2.5.1 We will begin by considering a more familiar situation; namely, the function $f(x) = x^2$, which takes a real number x as an input and produces its square x^2 as its output.

a. What is the value of $f(3)$?

b. Can we solve the equation $f(x) = 4$? If so, is the solution unique?

c. Can we solve the equation $f(x) = -10$? If so, is the solution unique?

d. Sketch a graph of the function $f(x) = x^2$ in Figure 2.5.1

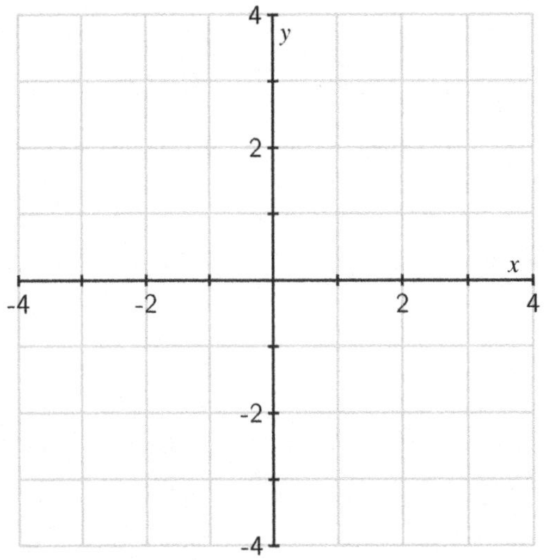

Figure 2.5.1 Graph the function $f(x) = x^2$ above.

e. We will now consider functions having the form $g(x) = mx$. Draw a graph of the function $g(x) = 2x$ on the left in Figure 2.5.2.

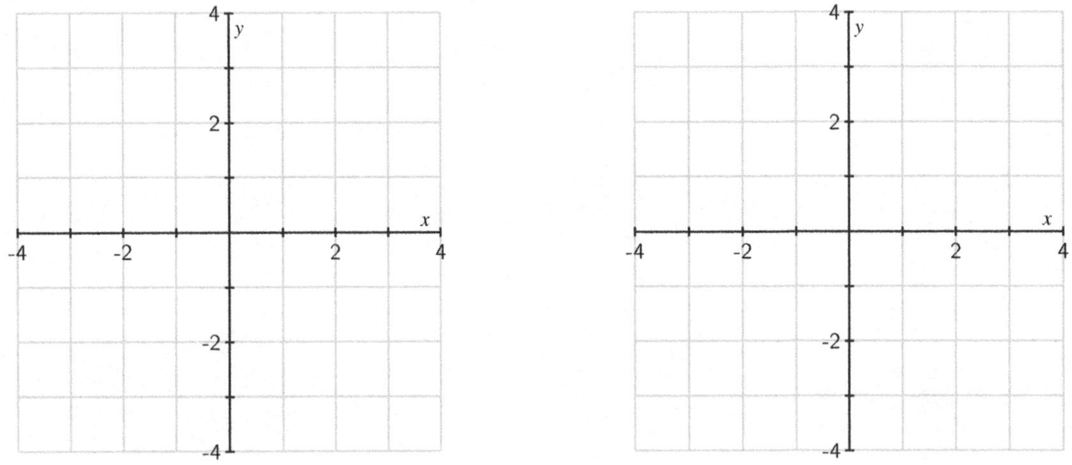

Figure 2.5.2 Graphs of the function $g(x) = 2x$ and $h(x) = -\frac{1}{3}x$.

f. Draw a graph of the function $h(x) = -\frac{1}{3}x$ on the right of Figure 2.5.2.

g. Remember that composing two functions means we use the output from one function as the input into the other; that is, $(g \circ h)(x) = g(h(x))$. What function results from composing $(g \circ h)(x)$?

Activity 2.5.2 In this activity, we will look at some examples of matrix transformations.

a. To begin, suppose that A is the matrix

$$A = \begin{bmatrix} 2 & 1 \\ 1 & 2 \end{bmatrix}.$$

with associated matrix transformation $T(\mathbf{x}) = A\mathbf{x}$.

1. What is $T\left(\begin{bmatrix} 1 \\ -2 \end{bmatrix}\right)$?
2. What is $T\left(\begin{bmatrix} 1 \\ 0 \end{bmatrix}\right)$?
3. What is $T\left(\begin{bmatrix} 0 \\ 1 \end{bmatrix}\right)$?
4. Is there a vector $\mathbf{x}$ such that $T(\mathbf{x}) = \begin{bmatrix} 3 \\ 0 \end{bmatrix}$?
5. Write $T\left(\begin{bmatrix} x \\ y \end{bmatrix}\right)$ as a two-dimensional vector.

b. Suppose that $T(\mathbf{x}) = A\mathbf{x}$ where

$$A = \begin{bmatrix} 3 & 3 & -2 & 1 \\ 0 & 2 & 1 & -3 \\ -2 & 1 & 4 & -4 \end{bmatrix}.$$

1. What is the dimension of the vectors $\mathbf{x}$ that are inputs for T?
2. What is the dimension of the vectors $T(\mathbf{x}) = A\mathbf{x}$ that are outputs?
3. If we describe this transformation as $T : \mathbb{R}^n \rightarrow \mathbb{R}^m$, what are the values of n and m and how do they relate to the shape of A?
4. Describe the vectors $\mathbf{x}$ for which $T(\mathbf{x}) = \mathbf{0}$.

c. If A is the matrix $A = \begin{bmatrix} \mathbf{v}_1 & \mathbf{v}_2 \end{bmatrix}$, what is $T\left(\begin{bmatrix} 1 \\ 0 \end{bmatrix}\right)$ in terms of the vectors $\mathbf{v}_1$ and $\mathbf{v}_2$? What about $T\left(\begin{bmatrix} 0 \\ 1 \end{bmatrix}\right)$?

d. Suppose that A is a 3×2 matrix and that $T(\mathbf{x}) = A\mathbf{x}$. If

$$T\left(\begin{bmatrix} 1 \\ 0 \end{bmatrix}\right) = \begin{bmatrix} 3 \\ -1 \\ 1 \end{bmatrix}, T\left(\begin{bmatrix} 0 \\ 1 \end{bmatrix}\right) = \begin{bmatrix} 2 \\ 2 \\ -1 \end{bmatrix},$$

what is the matrix A?

Activity 2.5.3 Let's look at some examples and apply these observations.

a. To begin, suppose that T is the matrix transformation that takes a two-dimensional vector $\mathbf{x}$ as an input and outputs $T(\mathbf{x})$, the two-dimensional vector obtained by rotating $\mathbf{x}$ counterclockwise by 90°, as shown in Figure 2.5.7.

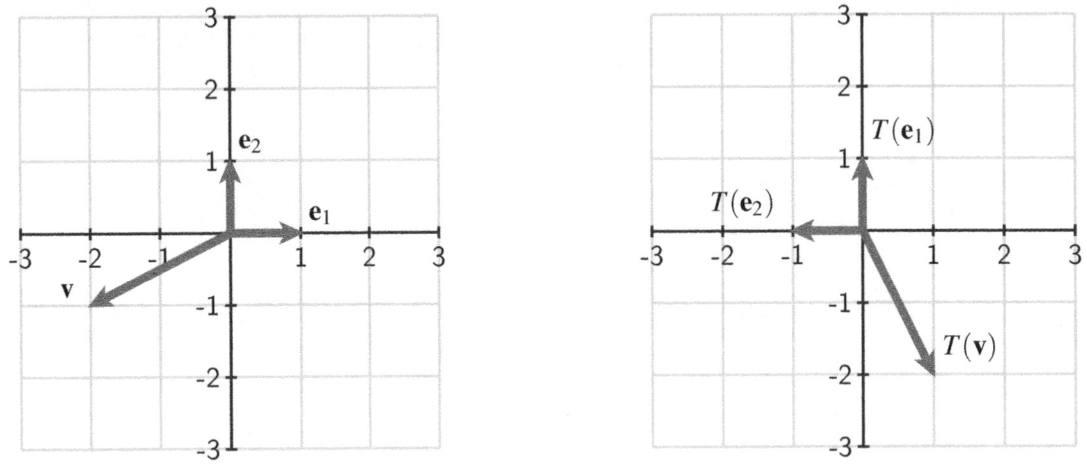

Figure 2.5.7 The matrix transformation T takes two-dimensional vectors on the left and rotates them by 90° counterclockwise into the vectors on the right.

We will see in the next section that many geometric operations like this one can be performed by matrix transformations.

1. If we write $T : \mathbb{R}^n \to \mathbb{R}^m$, what are the values of m and n, and what is the shape of the associated matrix A?
2. Determine the matrix A by applying Proposition 2.5.6.
3. If $\mathbf{v} = \begin{bmatrix} -2 \\ -1 \end{bmatrix}$ as shown on the left in Figure 2.5.7, use your matrix to determine $T(\mathbf{v})$ and verify that it agrees with that shown on the right of Figure 2.5.7.
4. If $\mathbf{x} = \begin{bmatrix} x \\ y \end{bmatrix}$, determine the vector $T(\mathbf{x})$ obtained by rotating $\mathbf{x}$ counterclockwise by 90°.

b. Suppose that we work for a company that makes baked goods, including cakes, doughnuts, and eclairs. The company operates two bakeries, Bakery 1 and Bakery 2. In one hour of operation,

- Bakery 1 produces 10 cakes, 50 doughnuts, and 30 eclairs.
- Bakery 2 produces 20 cakes, 30 doughnuts, and 30 eclairs.

If Bakery 1 operates for x_1 hours and Bakery 2 for x_2 hours, we will use the vector $\mathbf{x} = \begin{bmatrix} x_1 \\ x_2 \end{bmatrix}$ to describe the operation of the two bakeries.

We would like to describe a matrix transformation T where $\mathbf{x}$ describes the number of hours the bakeries operate and $T(\mathbf{x})$ describes the total number of cakes, doughnuts, and eclairs produced. That is, $T(\mathbf{x}) = \begin{bmatrix} y_1 \\ y_2 \\ y_3 \end{bmatrix}$ where y_1 is the number of cakes, y_2 is the number of doughnuts, and y_3 is the number of eclairs produced.

1. If $T : \mathbb{R}^n \to \mathbb{R}^m$, what are the values of m and n, and what is the shape of the associated matrix A?
2. We can determine the matrix A using Proposition 2.5.6. For instance, $T\left(\begin{bmatrix} 1 \\ 0 \end{bmatrix}\right)$ will describe the number of cakes, doughnuts, and eclairs produced when Bakery 1 operates for one hour and Bakery 2 sits idle. What is this vector?
3. In the same way, determine $T\left(\begin{bmatrix} 0 \\ 1 \end{bmatrix}\right)$. What is the matrix A?

4. If Bakery 1 operates for 120 hours and Bakery 2 for 180 hours, what is the total number of cakes, doughnuts, and eclairs produced?

5. Suppose that in one period of time, the company produces 5060 cakes, 14310 doughnuts, and 10470 eclairs. How long did each bakery operate?

6. Suppose that the company receives an order for a certain number of cakes, doughnuts, and eclairs. Can you guarantee that you can fill the order without having leftovers?

Activity 2.5.4 We will explore the composition of matrix transformations by revisiting the matrix transformations from Activity 2.5.3.

a. Let's begin with the matrix transformation $T : \mathbb{R}^2 \to \mathbb{R}^2$ that rotates a two-dimensional vector $\mathbf{x}$ by 90° to produce $T(\mathbf{x})$. We saw in the earlier activity that the associated matrix is $A = \begin{bmatrix} 0 & -1 \\ 1 & 0 \end{bmatrix}$. Suppose that we compose this matrix transformation with itself to obtain $(T \circ T)(\mathbf{x}) = T(T(\mathbf{x}))$, which is the result of rotating $\mathbf{x}$ by 90° twice.

   1. What is the matrix associated to the composition $(T \circ T)$?

   2. What is the result of rotating $\mathbf{v} = \begin{bmatrix} -2 \\ -1 \end{bmatrix}$ twice?

   3. Suppose that $R : \mathbb{R}^2 \to \mathbb{R}^2$ is the matrix transformation that rotates vectors by 180°, as shown in Figure 2.5.9.

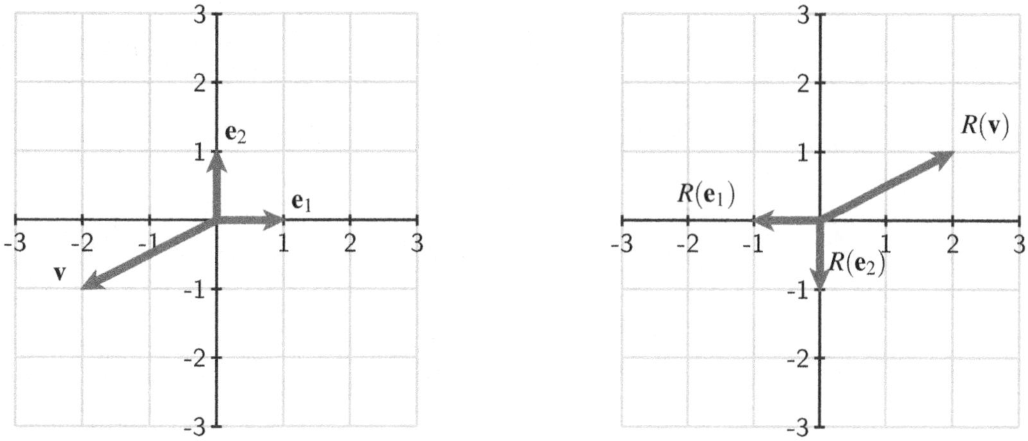

Figure 2.5.9 The matrix transformation R takes two-dimensional vectors on the left and rotates them by 180° into the vectors on the right.

Use Proposition 2.5.6 to find the matrix associated to R and explain why it is the same matrix associated to $(T \circ T)$.

   4. Write the two-dimensional vector $(T \circ T)\left(\begin{bmatrix} x \\ y \end{bmatrix}\right)$. How might this vector be expressed in terms of scalar multiplication and why does this make sense geometrically?

b. In the previous activity, we imagined a company that operates two bakeries. We found the matrix transformation $T : \mathbb{R}^2 \to \mathbb{R}^3$ where $T\left(\begin{bmatrix} x_1 \\ x_2 \end{bmatrix}\right)$ describes the number of cakes, doughnuts, and eclairs when Bakery1 runs for x_1 hours and Bakery 2 runs for x_2 hours. The associated matrix is $A = \begin{bmatrix} 10 & 20 \\ 50 & 30 \\ 30 & 30 \end{bmatrix}$.

   Suppose now that

   - Each cake requires 4 cups of flour and and 2 cups of sugar.
   - Each doughnut requires 1 cup of flour and 1 cup of sugar.
   - Each eclair requires 1 cup of flour and 2 cups of sugar.

   We will describe a matrix transformation $S : \mathbb{R}^3 \to \mathbb{R}^2$ where $S\left(\begin{bmatrix} y_1 \\ y_2 \\ y_3 \end{bmatrix}\right)$ is a two-dimensional vector describing the number of cups of flour and sugar required to make y_1 cakes, y_2 doughnuts, and y_3 eclairs.

   1. Use Proposition 2.5.6 to write the matrix B associated to the transformation S.

2. If we make 1200 cakes, 2850 doughnuts, and 2250 eclairs, how many cups of flour and sugar are required?

3. Suppose that Bakery 1 operates for 75 hours and Bakery 2 operates for 53 hours. How many cakes, doughnuts, and eclairs are produced? How many cups of flour and sugar are required?
4. What is the meaning of the composition $(S \circ T)$ and what is its associated matrix?
5. In a certain time interval, both bakeries use a total of 5800 cups of flour and 5980 cups of sugar. How long have the two bakeries been operating?

Activity 2.5.5 Suppose we run a company that has two warehouses, which we will call P and Q, and a fleet of 1000 delivery trucks. Every morning, a delivery truck goes out from one of the warehouses and returns in the evening to one of the warehouses. It is observed that

- 70% of the trucks that leave P return to P. The other 30% return to Q.
- 50% of the trucks that leave Q return to Q and 50% return to P.

The distribution of trucks is represented by the vector $\mathbf{x} = \begin{bmatrix} x_1 \\ x_2 \end{bmatrix}$ when there are x_1 trucks at location P and x_2 trucks at Q. If $\mathbf{x}$ describes the distribution of trucks in the morning, then the matrix transformation $T(\mathbf{x})$ will describe the distribution in the evening.

a. Suppose that all 1000 trucks begin the day at location P and none at Q. How many trucks are at each location that evening? Using our vector representation, what is $T\left(\begin{bmatrix} 1000 \\ 0 \end{bmatrix}\right)$?

   So that we can find the matrix A associated to T, what does this tell us about $T\left(\begin{bmatrix} 1 \\ 0 \end{bmatrix}\right)$?

b. In the same way, suppose that all 1000 trucks begin the day at location Q and none at P. How many trucks are at each location that evening? What is the result $T\left(\begin{bmatrix} 0 \\ 1000 \end{bmatrix}\right)$ and what is $T\left(\begin{bmatrix} 0 \\ 1 \end{bmatrix}\right)$?

c. Find the matrix A such that $T(\mathbf{x}) = A\mathbf{x}$.

d. Suppose that there are 100 trucks at P and 900 at Q in the morning. How many are there at the two locations in the evening?

e. Suppose that there are 550 trucks at P and 450 at Q in the evening. How many trucks were there at the two locations that morning?

f. Suppose that all of the trucks are at location Q on Monday morning.

   1. How many trucks are at each location Monday evening?
   2. How many trucks are at each location Tuesday evening?
   3. How many trucks are at each location Wednesday evening?

g. Suppose that S is the matrix transformation that transforms the distribution of trucks $\mathbf{x}$ one morning into the distribution of trucks in the morning one week (seven days) later. What is the matrix that defines the transformation S?

2.6 The geometry of matrix transformations

Preview Activity 2.6.1 We will describe the matrix transformation T that reflects 2-dimensional vectors across the horizontal axis. For instance, Figure 2.6.1 illustrates how a vector $\mathbf{x}$ is reflected onto the vector $T(\mathbf{x})$.

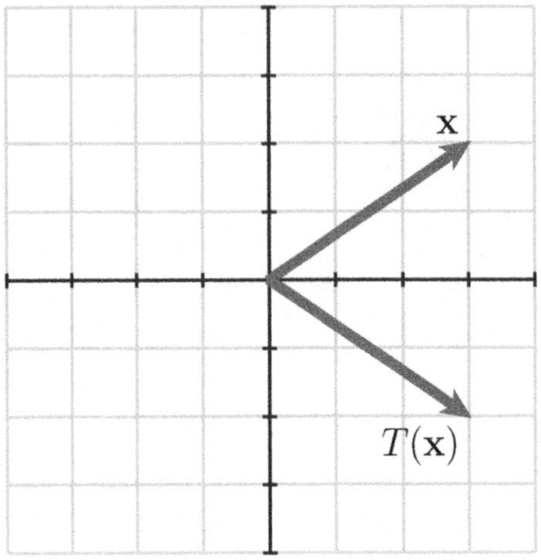

Figure 2.6.1 A vector $\mathbf{x}$ and its reflection $T(\mathbf{x})$ across the horizontal axis.

a. If $\mathbf{x} = \begin{bmatrix} 2 \\ 4 \end{bmatrix}$, what is the vector $T(\mathbf{x})$? Sketch the vectors $\mathbf{x}$ and $T(\mathbf{x})$.

b. More generally, if $\mathbf{x} = \begin{bmatrix} x \\ y \end{bmatrix}$, what is $T(\mathbf{x})$?

c. Find the vectors $T\left(\begin{bmatrix} 1 \\ 0 \end{bmatrix}\right)$ and $T\left(\begin{bmatrix} 0 \\ 1 \end{bmatrix}\right)$.

d. Use your results to write the matrix A so that $T(\mathbf{x}) = A\mathbf{x}$. Then verify that $T\left(\begin{bmatrix} x \\ y \end{bmatrix}\right)$ agrees with what you found in part b.

e. Describe the transformation that results from composing T with itself; that is, what is the transformation $T \circ T$? Explain how matrix multiplication can be used to justify your response.

Activity 2.6.2 Using matrix transformations to describe geometric operations.

This activity uses an interactive diagram that is available at `gvsu.edu/s/0Jf`.

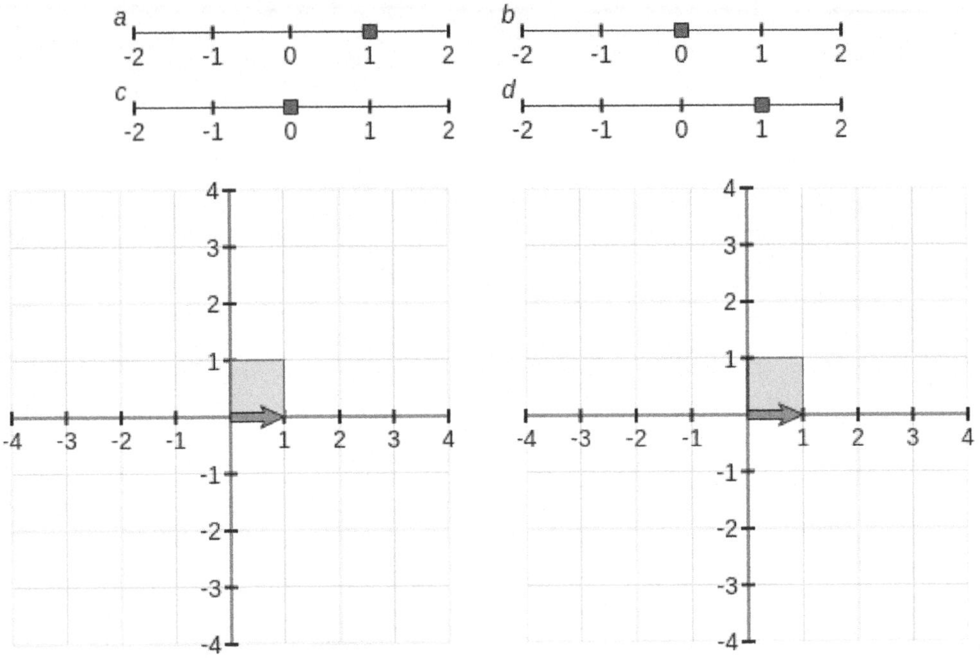

Figure 2.6.2 The matrix transformation T transforms features shown on the left into features shown on the right.

For the following 2×2 matrices A, use the diagram to study the effect of the corresponding matrix transformation $T(\mathbf{x}) = A\mathbf{x}$. For each transformation, describe the geometric effect the transformation has on the plane.

a. $A = \begin{bmatrix} 2 & 0 \\ 0 & 1 \end{bmatrix}$.

b. $A = \begin{bmatrix} 2 & 0 \\ 0 & 2 \end{bmatrix}$.

c. $A = \begin{bmatrix} 0 & 1 \\ -1 & 0 \end{bmatrix}$.

d. $A = \begin{bmatrix} 1 & 1 \\ 0 & 1 \end{bmatrix}$.

e. $A = \begin{bmatrix} -1 & 0 \\ 0 & 1 \end{bmatrix}$.

f. $A = \begin{bmatrix} 1 & 0 \\ 0 & 0 \end{bmatrix}$.

g. $A = \begin{bmatrix} 1 & 0 \\ 0 & 1 \end{bmatrix}$.

h. $A = \begin{bmatrix} 1 & -1 \\ -2 & 2 \end{bmatrix}$.

Activity 2.6.3 In this activity, we seek to describe various matrix transformations by finding the matrix that gives the desired transformation. All of the transformations that we study here have the form $T : \mathbb{R}^2 \to \mathbb{R}^2$.

a. Find the matrix of the transformation that has no effect on vectors; that is, $T(\mathbf{x}) = \mathbf{x}$.

b. Find the matrix of the transformation that reflects vectors in $\mathbb{R}^2$ across the line $y = x$.

c. What is the result of composing the reflection you found in the previous part with itself; that is, what is the effect of reflecting across the line $y = x$ and then reflecting across this line again? Provide a geometric explanation for your result as well as an algebraic one obtained by multiplying matrices.

d. Find the matrix that rotates vectors counterclockwise in the plane by $90°$.

e. Compare the result of rotating by $90°$ and then reflecting in the line $y = x$ to the result of first reflecting in $y = x$ and then rotating $90°$.

f. Find the matrix that results from composing a $90°$ rotation with itself four times; that is, if T is the matrix transformation that rotates vectors by $90°$, find the matrix for $T \circ T \circ T \circ T$. Explain why your result makes sense geometrically.

g. Explain why the matrix that rotates vectors counterclockwise by an angle θ is

$$\begin{bmatrix} \cos\theta & -\sin\theta \\ \sin\theta & \cos\theta \end{bmatrix}.$$

Activity 2.6.4 In this activity, we will use homogeneous coordinates and matrix transformations to move our character into a variety of poses.

a. Since we regard our character as living in $\mathbb{R}^3$, we will consider matrix transformations defined by matrices

$$\begin{bmatrix} a & b & c \\ d & e & f \\ 0 & 0 & 1 \end{bmatrix}.$$

Verify that such a matrix transformation transforms points in the plane $z = 1$ into points in the same plane; that is, verify that

$$\begin{bmatrix} a & b & c \\ d & e & f \\ 0 & 0 & 1 \end{bmatrix} \begin{bmatrix} x \\ y \\ 1 \end{bmatrix} = \begin{bmatrix} x' \\ y' \\ 1 \end{bmatrix}.$$

Express the coordinates of the resulting point x' and y' in terms of the coordinates of the original point x and y.

This activity uses an interactive diagram that is available at `gvsu.edu/s/0Jb`. Using the six sliders, you may choose the matrix $\begin{bmatrix} a & b & c \\ d & e & f \\ 0 & 0 & 1 \end{bmatrix}$ that will move our character in the plane.

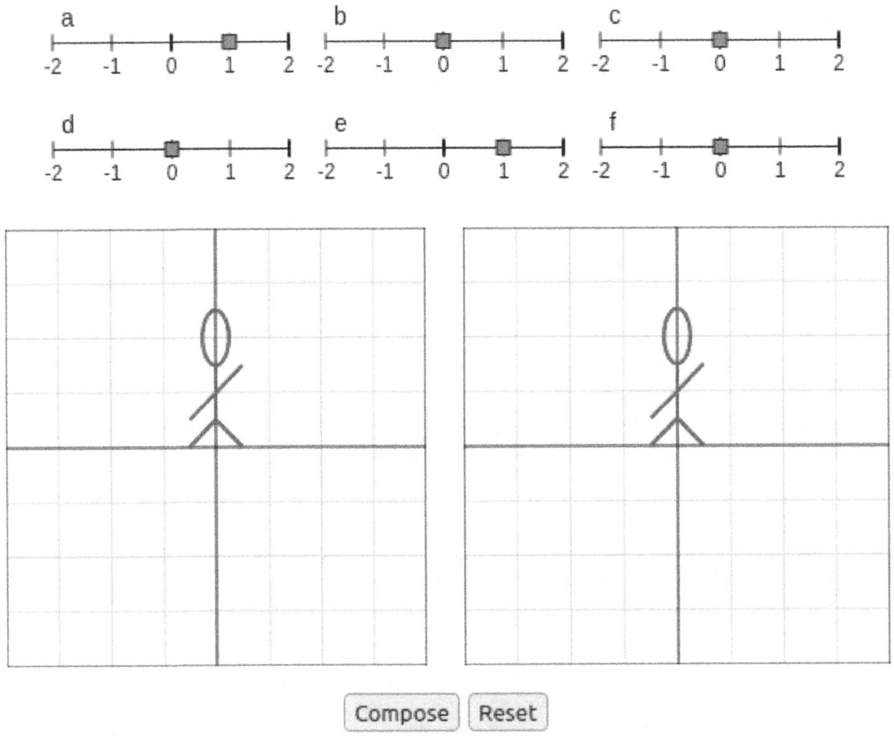

Figure 2.6.13 An interactive diagram that allows us to move the character using homogeneous coordinates.

b. Find the matrix transformation that translates our character to a new position in the plane, as shown in Figure 2.6.14

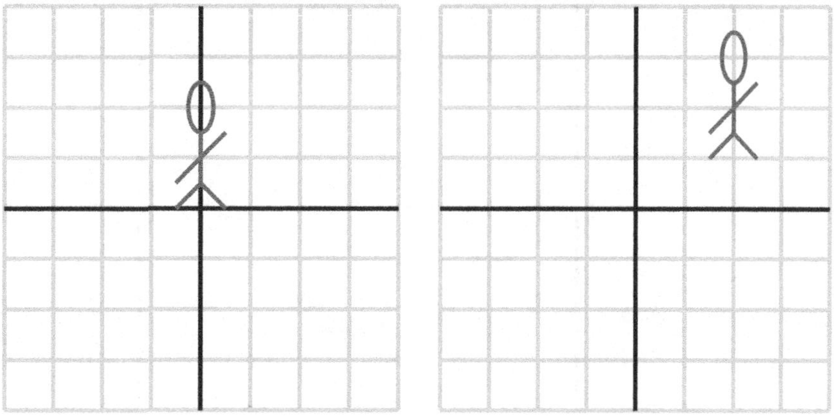

Figure 2.6.14 Translating to a new position.

c. As originally drawn, our character is waving with one of their hands. In one of the movie's scenes, we would like them to wave with their other hand, as shown in Figure 2.6.15. Find the matrix transformation that moves them into this pose.

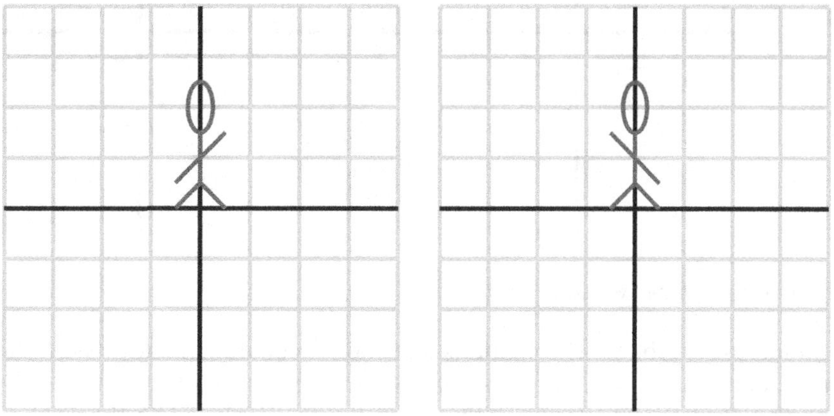

Figure 2.6.15 Waving with the other hand.

d. Later, our character performs a cartwheel by moving through the sequence of poses shown in Figure 2.6.16. Find the matrix transformations that create these poses.

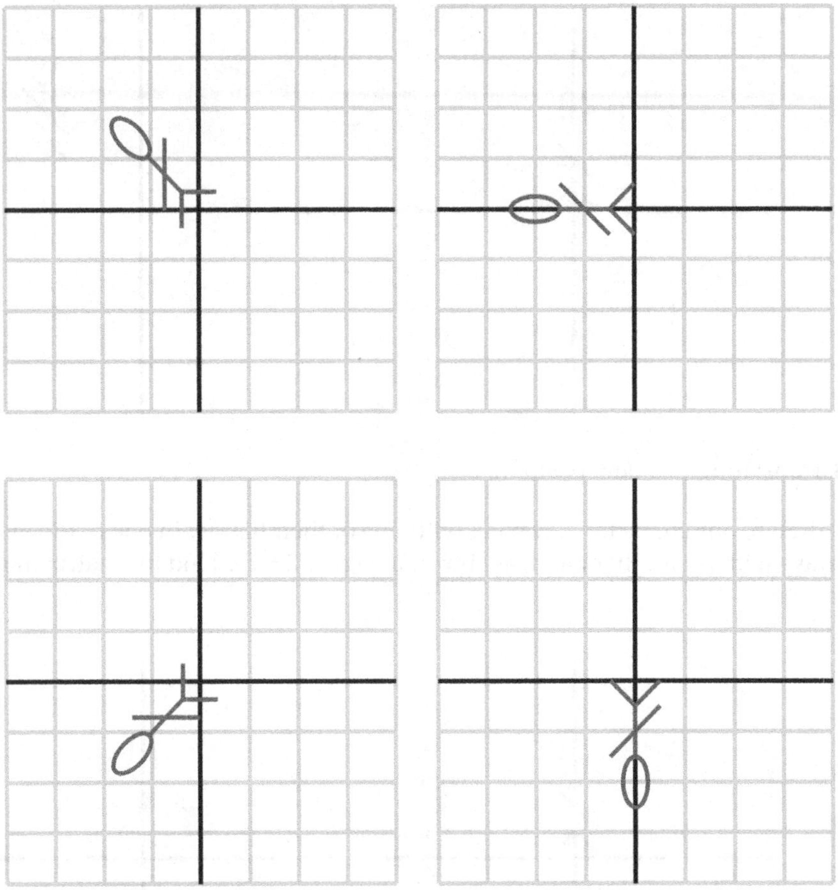

Figure 2.6.16 Performing a cartwheel.

e. Next, we would like to find the transformations that zoom in on our character's face, as shown in Figure 2.6.17. To do this, you should think about composing matrix transformations. This can be accomplished in the diagram by using the *Compose* button, which makes the current pose, displayed on the right, the new beginning pose, displayed on the left. What is the matrix transformation that moves the character from the original pose, shown in the upper left, to the final pose, shown in the lower right?

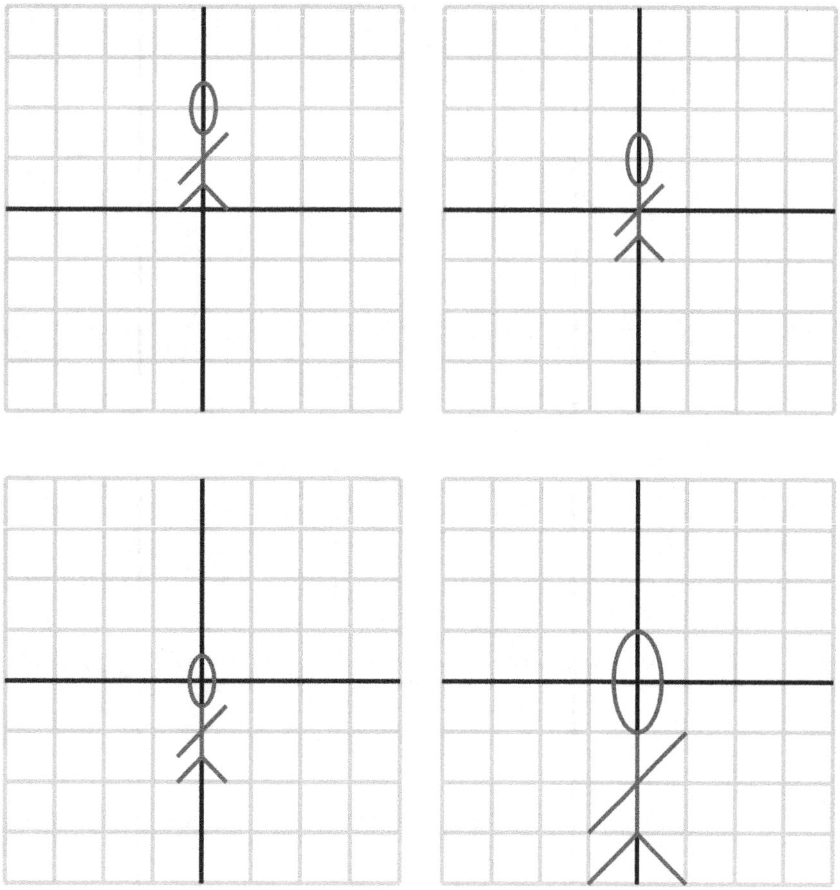

Figure 2.6.17 Zooming in on our characters' face.

f. We would also like to create our character's shadow, shown in the sequence of poses in Figure 2.6.18. Find the sequence of matrix transformations that achieves this. In particular, find the matrix transformation that takes our character from their original pose to their shadow in the lower right.

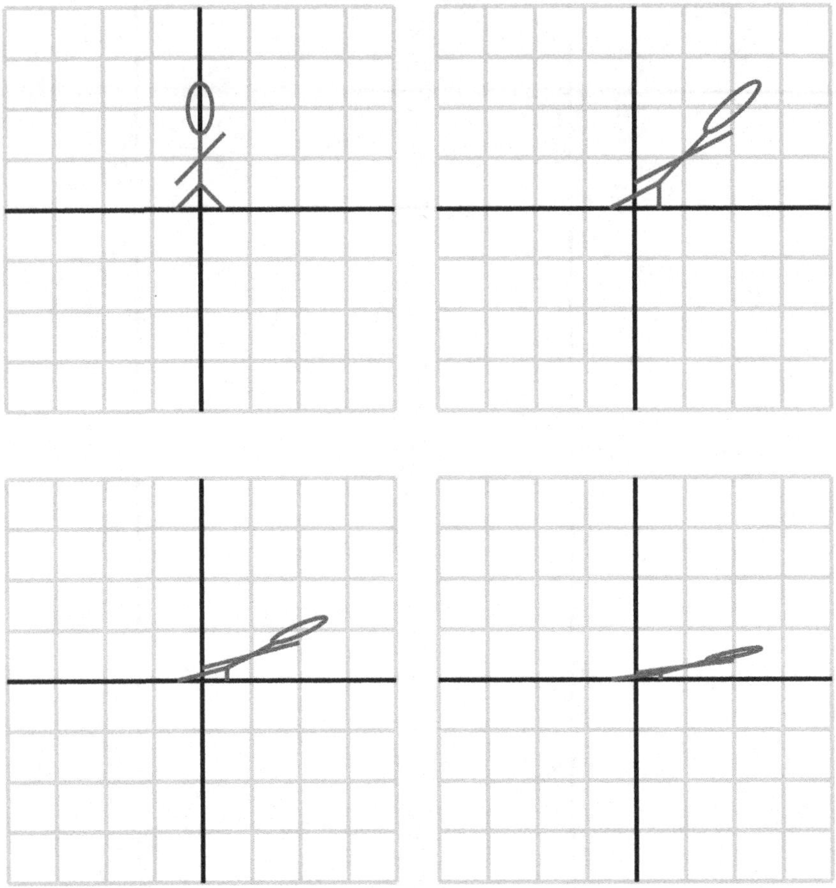

Figure 2.6.18 Casting a shadow.

g. Write a final scene to the movie and describe how to construct a sequence of matrix transformations that create your scene.

3 *Invertibility, bases, and coordinate systems*

3.1 Invertibility

Preview Activity 3.1.1

a. Explain how you would solve the equation $3x = 5$ using multiplication rather than division.

b. Find the 2×2 matrix A that rotates vectors counterclockwise by $90°$.

c. Find the 2×2 matrix B that rotates vectors *clockwise* by $90°$.

d. What do you expect the product AB to be? Explain the reasoning behind your expectation and then compute AB to verify it.

e. Solve the equation $A\mathbf{x} = \begin{bmatrix} 3 \\ -2 \end{bmatrix}$ using Gaussian elimination.

f. Explain why your solution may also be found by computing $\mathbf{x} = B\begin{bmatrix} 3 \\ -2 \end{bmatrix}$.

Activity 3.1.2 This activity demonstrates a procedure for finding the inverse of a matrix A.

a. Suppose that $A = \begin{bmatrix} 3 & -2 \\ 1 & -1 \end{bmatrix}$. To find an inverse B, we write its columns as $B = \begin{bmatrix} \mathbf{b}_1 & \mathbf{b}_2 \end{bmatrix}$ and require that

$$AB = I$$

$$\begin{bmatrix} A\mathbf{b}_1 & A\mathbf{b}_2 \end{bmatrix} = \begin{bmatrix} 1 & 0 \\ 0 & 1 \end{bmatrix}.$$

In other words, we can find the columns of B by solving the equations

$$A\mathbf{b}_1 = \begin{bmatrix} 1 \\ 0 \end{bmatrix}, \quad A\mathbf{b}_2 = \begin{bmatrix} 0 \\ 1 \end{bmatrix}.$$

Solve these equations to find $\mathbf{b}_1$ and $\mathbf{b}_2$. Then write the matrix B and verify that $AB = I$. This is enough for us to conclude that B is the inverse of A.

b. Find the product BA and explain why we now know that B is invertible and $B^{-1} = A$.

c. What happens when you try to find the inverse of $C = \begin{bmatrix} -2 & 1 \\ 4 & -2 \end{bmatrix}$?

d. We now develop a condition that must be satisfied by an invertible matrix. Suppose that A is an invertible $n \times n$ matrix with inverse B and suppose that $\mathbf{b}$ is any n-dimensional vector. Since $AB = I$, we have

$$A(B\mathbf{b}) = (AB)\mathbf{b} = I\mathbf{b} = \mathbf{b}.$$

This says that the equation $A\mathbf{x} = \mathbf{b}$ is consistent and that $\mathbf{x} = B\mathbf{b}$ is a solution.

Since we know that $A\mathbf{x} = \mathbf{b}$ is consistent for any vector $\mathbf{b}$, what does this say about the span of the columns of A?

e. Since A is a square matrix, what does this say about the pivot positions of A? What is the reduced row echelon form of A?

f. In this activity, we have studied the matrices

$$A = \begin{bmatrix} 3 & -2 \\ 1 & -1 \end{bmatrix}, \quad C = \begin{bmatrix} -2 & 1 \\ 4 & -2 \end{bmatrix}.$$

Find the reduced row echelon form of each and explain how those forms enable us to conclude that one matrix is invertible and the other is not.

Activity 3.1.3 We'll begin by considering the square matrix

$$A = \begin{bmatrix} 1 & 0 & 2 \\ 2 & 2 & 1 \\ 1 & 1 & 1 \end{bmatrix}.$$

a. Describe the solution space to the equation $A\mathbf{x} = \begin{bmatrix} 3 \\ 4 \\ 3 \end{bmatrix}$ by augmenting A and finding the reduced row echelon form.

b. Using Proposition 3.1.5, explain why A is invertible and find its inverse.

c. Now use the inverse to solve the equation $A\mathbf{x} = \begin{bmatrix} 3 \\ 4 \\ 3 \end{bmatrix}$ and verify that your result agrees with what you found in part a.

d. If you have defined a matrix `B` in Sage, you can find it's inverse as `B.inverse()` or `B^-1`. Use Sage to find the inverse of the matrix

$$B = \begin{bmatrix} 1 & -2 & -1 \\ -1 & 5 & 6 \\ 5 & -4 & 6 \end{bmatrix}$$

and use it to solve the equation $B\mathbf{x} = \begin{bmatrix} 8 \\ 3 \\ 36 \end{bmatrix}$.

e. If A and B are the two matrices defined in this activity, find their product AB and verify that it is invertible.

f. Compute the products $A^{-1}B^{-1}$ and $B^{-1}A^{-1}$. Which one agrees with $(AB)^{-1}$?

g. Explain your finding by considering the product

$$(AB)(B^{-1}A^{-1})$$

and using associativity to regroup the products so that the middle two terms are multiplied first.

Activity 3.1.4 Gaussian elimination and matrix multiplication. This activity explores how the row operations of scaling, interchange, and replacement can be performed using matrix multiplication.

As an example, we consider the matrix

$$A = \begin{bmatrix} 1 & 2 & 1 \\ 2 & 0 & -2 \\ -1 & 2 & -1 \end{bmatrix}$$

and apply a replacement operation that multiplies the first row by -2 and adds it to the second row. Rather than performing this operation in the usual way, we construct a new matrix by applying the desired replacement operation to the identity matrix. To illustrate, we begin with the identity matrix

$$I = \begin{bmatrix} 1 & 0 & 0 \\ 0 & 1 & 0 \\ 0 & 0 & 1 \end{bmatrix}$$

and form a new matrix by multiplying the first row by -2 and adding it to the second row to obtain

$$R = \begin{bmatrix} 1 & 0 & 0 \\ -2 & 1 & 0 \\ 0 & 0 & 1 \end{bmatrix}.$$

a. Show that the product RA is the result of applying the replacement operation to A.

b. Explain why R is invertible and find its inverse R^{-1}.

c. Describe the relationship between R and R^{-1} and use the connection to replacement operations to explain why it holds.

d. Other row operations can be performed using a similar procedure. For instance, suppose we want to scale the second row of A by 4. Find a matrix S so that SA is the same as that obtained from the scaling operation. Why is S invertible and what is S^{-1}?

e. Finally, suppose we want to interchange the first and third rows of A. Find a matrix P, usually called a *permutation matrix* that performs this operation. What is P^{-1}?

f. The original matrix A is seen to be row equivalent to the upper triangular matrix U by performing three replacement operations on A:

$$A = \begin{bmatrix} 1 & 2 & 1 \\ 2 & 0 & -2 \\ -1 & 2 & -1 \end{bmatrix} \sim \begin{bmatrix} 1 & 2 & 1 \\ 0 & -4 & -4 \\ 0 & 0 & -4 \end{bmatrix} = U.$$

Find the matrices L_1, L_2, and L_3 that perform these row replacement operations so that $L_3L_2L_1A = U$.

g. Explain why the matrix product $L_3L_2L_1$ is invertible and use this fact to write $A = LU$. What is the matrix L that you find? Why do you think we denote it by L?

3.2 Bases and coordinate systems

Preview Activity 3.2.1 Consider the vectors

$$\mathbf{v}_1 = \begin{bmatrix} 2 \\ 1 \end{bmatrix}, \mathbf{v}_2 = \begin{bmatrix} 1 \\ 2 \end{bmatrix}$$

in $\mathbb{R}^2$, which are shown in Figure 3.2.2.

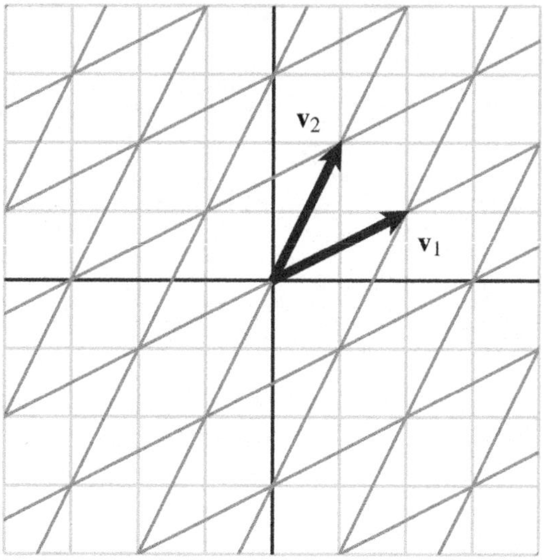

Figure 3.2.2 Linear combinations of $\mathbf{v}_1$ and $\mathbf{v}_2$.

a. Indicate the linear combination $\mathbf{v}_1 - 2\mathbf{v}_2$ on the figure.

b. Express the vector $\begin{bmatrix} -3 \\ 0 \end{bmatrix}$ as a linear combination of $\mathbf{v}_1$ and $\mathbf{v}_2$.

c. Find the linear combination $10\mathbf{v}_1 - 13\mathbf{v}_2$.

d. Express the vector $\begin{bmatrix} 16 \\ -4 \end{bmatrix}$ as a linear combination of $\mathbf{v}_1$ and $\mathbf{v}_2$.

e. Explain why every vector in $\mathbb{R}^2$ can be written as a linear combination of $\mathbf{v}_1$ and $\mathbf{v}_2$ in exactly one way.

Activity 3.2.2 We will look at some examples of bases in this activity.

a. In the preview activity, we worked with the set of vectors in $\mathbb{R}^2$:

$$\mathbf{v}_1 = \begin{bmatrix} 2 \\ 1 \end{bmatrix}, \mathbf{v}_2 = \begin{bmatrix} 1 \\ 2 \end{bmatrix}.$$

Explain why these vectors form a basis for $\mathbb{R}^2$.

b. Consider the set of vectors in $\mathbb{R}^3$

$$\mathbf{v}_1 = \begin{bmatrix} 1 \\ 1 \\ 1 \end{bmatrix}, \mathbf{v}_2 = \begin{bmatrix} 0 \\ 1 \\ -1 \end{bmatrix}, \mathbf{v}_3 = \begin{bmatrix} 1 \\ 0 \\ -1 \end{bmatrix}$$

and determine whether they form a basis for $\mathbb{R}^3$.

c. Do the vectors

$$\mathbf{v}_1 = \begin{bmatrix} -2 \\ 1 \\ 3 \end{bmatrix}, \mathbf{v}_2 = \begin{bmatrix} 3 \\ 0 \\ -1 \end{bmatrix}, \mathbf{v}_3 = \begin{bmatrix} 1 \\ 1 \\ 0 \end{bmatrix}, \mathbf{v}_4 = \begin{bmatrix} 0 \\ 3 \\ -2 \end{bmatrix}$$

form a basis for $\mathbb{R}^3$?

d. Explain why the vectors $\mathbf{e}_1, \mathbf{e}_2, \mathbf{e}_3$ form a basis for $\mathbb{R}^3$.

e. If a set of vectors $\mathbf{v}_1, \mathbf{v}_2, \ldots, \mathbf{v}_n$ forms a basis for $\mathbb{R}^m$, what can you guarantee about the pivot positions of the matrix

$$\begin{bmatrix} \mathbf{v}_1 & \mathbf{v}_2 & \ldots & \mathbf{v}_n \end{bmatrix}?$$

f. If the set of vectors $\mathbf{v}_1, \mathbf{v}_2, \ldots, \mathbf{v}_n$ is a basis for $\mathbb{R}^{10}$, how many vectors must be in the set?

[illegible]

Activity 3.2.3 Let's begin with the basis $\mathcal{B} = \{\mathbf{v}_1, \mathbf{v}_2\}$ of $\mathbb{R}^2$ where

$$\mathbf{v}_1 = \begin{bmatrix} 3 \\ -2 \end{bmatrix}, \mathbf{v}_2 = \begin{bmatrix} 2 \\ 1 \end{bmatrix}.$$

a. If the coordinates of $\mathbf{x}$ in the basis $\mathcal{B}$ are $\{\mathbf{x}\}_{\mathcal{B}} = \begin{bmatrix} -2 \\ 4 \end{bmatrix}$, what is the vector $\mathbf{x}$?

b. If $\mathbf{x} = \begin{bmatrix} 3 \\ 5 \end{bmatrix}$, find the coordinates of $\mathbf{x}$ in the basis $\mathcal{B}$; that is, find $\{\mathbf{x}\}_{\mathcal{B}}$.

c. Find a matrix A such that, for any vector $\mathbf{x}$, we have $\mathbf{x} = A\{\mathbf{x}\}_{\mathcal{B}}$. Explain why this matrix is invertible.

d. Using what you found in the previous part, find a matrix B such that, for any vector $\mathbf{x}$, we have $\{\mathbf{x}\}_{\mathcal{B}} = B\mathbf{x}$. What is the relationship between the two matrices A and B? Explain why this relationship holds.

e. Suppose we consider the standard basis

$$\mathcal{E} = \{\mathbf{e}_1, \mathbf{e}_2\}.$$

What is the relationship between $\mathbf{x}$ and $\{\mathbf{x}\}_{\mathcal{E}}$?

f. Suppose we also consider the basis

$$\mathcal{C} = \left\{ \begin{bmatrix} 1 \\ 2 \end{bmatrix}, \begin{bmatrix} -2 \\ 1 \end{bmatrix} \right\}.$$

Find a matrix C that converts coordinates in the basis $\mathcal{C}$ into coordinates in the basis $\mathcal{B}$; that is,

$$\{\mathbf{x}\}_{\mathcal{B}} = C\{\mathbf{x}\}_{\mathcal{C}}.$$

You may wish to think about converting coordinates from the basis $\mathcal{C}$ into the standard coordinate system and then into the basis $\mathcal{B}$.

Activity 3.2.4 Edge detection. An important problem in the field of computer vision is to detect edges in a digital photograph, as is shown in Figure 3.2.12. Edge detection algorithms are useful when, say, we want a robot to locate an object in its field of view. Graphic designers also use these algorithms to create artistic effects.

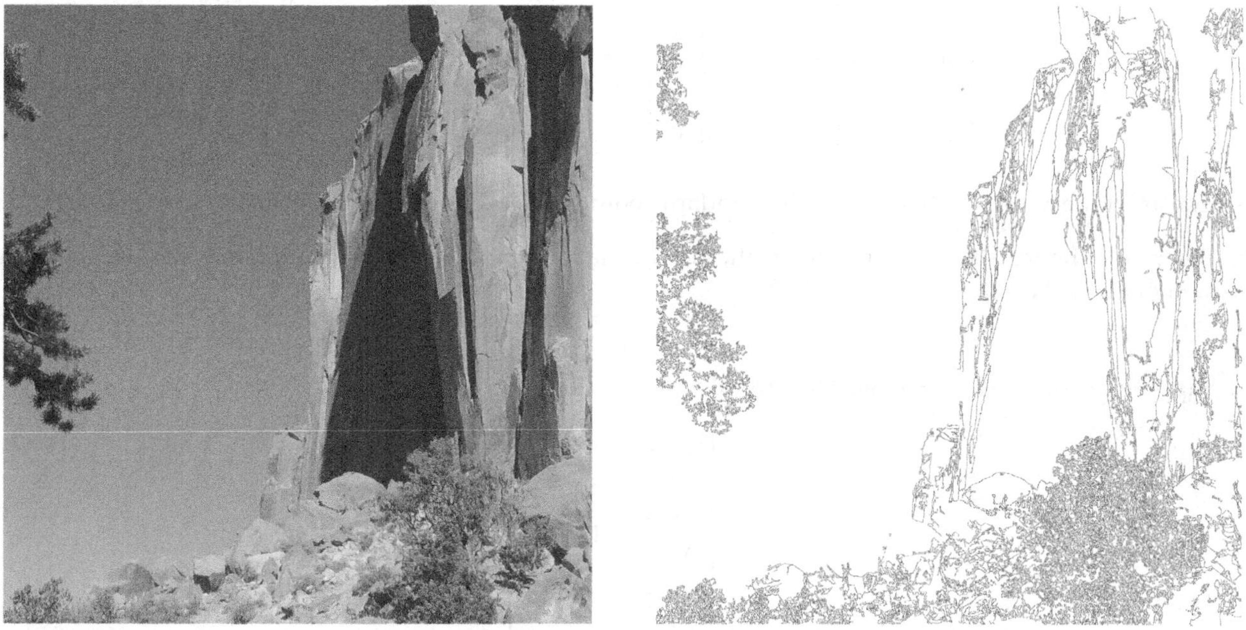

Figure 3.2.12 A canyon wall in Capitol Reef National Park and the result of an edge detection algorithm.

We will consider a very simple version of an edge detection algorithm to give a sense of how this works. Rather than considering a two-dimensional photograph, we will think about a one-dimensional row of pixels in a photograph. The grayscale values of a pixel measure the brightness of a pixel; a grayscale value of 0 corresponds to black, and a value of 255 corresponds to white.

Suppose, for simplicity, that the grayscale values for a row of six pixels are represented by a vector $\mathbf{x}$ in $\mathbb{R}^6$:

$$\mathbf{x} = \begin{bmatrix} 25 \\ 34 \\ 30 \\ 45 \\ 190 \\ 200 \end{bmatrix}.$$

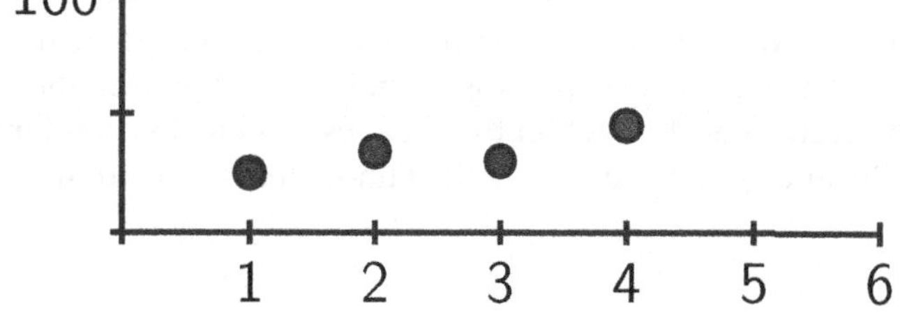

We can easily see that there is a jump in brightness between pixels 4 and 5, but how can we detect it computationally?

We will introduce a new basis $\mathcal{B}$ for $\mathbb{R}^6$ with vectors:

$$\mathbf{v}_1 = \begin{bmatrix} 1 \\ 0 \\ 0 \\ 0 \\ 0 \\ 0 \end{bmatrix}, \mathbf{v}_2 = \begin{bmatrix} 1 \\ 1 \\ 0 \\ 0 \\ 0 \\ 0 \end{bmatrix}, \mathbf{v}_3 = \begin{bmatrix} 1 \\ 1 \\ 1 \\ 0 \\ 0 \\ 0 \end{bmatrix}, \mathbf{v}_4 = \begin{bmatrix} 1 \\ 1 \\ 1 \\ 1 \\ 0 \\ 0 \end{bmatrix}, \mathbf{v}_5 = \begin{bmatrix} 1 \\ 1 \\ 1 \\ 1 \\ 1 \\ 0 \end{bmatrix}, \mathbf{v}_6 = \begin{bmatrix} 1 \\ 1 \\ 1 \\ 1 \\ 1 \\ 1 \end{bmatrix}.$$

a. Construct the matrix $P_{\mathcal{B}}$ that relates the standard coordinate system with the coordinates in the basis $\mathcal{B}$.

b. Determine the matrix $P_{\mathcal{B}}^{-1}$ that converts the representation of $\mathbf{x}$ in standard coordinates into the coordinate system defined by $\mathcal{B}$.

c. Suppose the vectors are expressed in general terms as

$$\mathbf{x} = \begin{bmatrix} x_1 \\ x_2 \\ x_3 \\ x_4 \\ x_5 \\ x_6 \end{bmatrix}, \quad \{\mathbf{x}\}_{\mathcal{B}} = \begin{bmatrix} c_1 \\ c_2 \\ c_3 \\ c_4 \\ c_5 \\ c_6 \end{bmatrix}.$$

Using the relationship $\{\mathbf{x}\}_{\mathcal{B}} = P_{\mathcal{B}}^{-1}\mathbf{x}$, determine an expression for the coefficient c_2 in terms of $x_1, x_2, \ldots, x_6$. What does c_2 measure in terms of the grayscale values of the pixels? What does c_4 measure in terms of the grayscale values of the pixels?

d. Now for the specific vector

$$\mathbf{x} = \begin{bmatrix} 25 \\ 34 \\ 30 \\ 45 \\ 190 \\ 200 \end{bmatrix},$$

determine the representation of $\mathbf{x}$ in the $\mathcal{B}$-coordinate system.

e. Explain how the coefficients in $\{\mathbf{x}\}_{\mathcal{B}}$ determine the location of the jump in brightness in the grayscale values represented by the vector $\mathbf{x}$.

Readers who are familiar with calculus may recognize that this change of basis converts a vector $\mathbf{x}$ into $\{\mathbf{x}\}_{\mathcal{B}}$, the set of changes in $\mathbf{x}$. This process is similar to differentiation in calculus. Similarly, the process of converting $\{\mathbf{x}\}_{\mathcal{B}}$ into the vector $\mathbf{x}$ adds together the changes in a process similar to integration. As a result, this change of basis represents a linear algebraic version of the Fundamental Theorem of Calculus.

3.3 Image compression

Preview Activity 3.3.1 Since we will be using various bases and the coordinate systems they define, let's review how to translate between coordinate systems.

a. Suppose that we have a basis $\mathcal{B} = \{\mathbf{v}_1, \mathbf{v}_2, \ldots, \mathbf{v}_m\}$ for $\mathbb{R}^m$. Explain what we mean by the representation $\{\mathbf{x}\}_{\mathcal{B}}$ of a vector $\mathbf{x}$ in the coordinate system defined by $\mathcal{B}$.

b. If we are given the representation $\{\mathbf{x}\}_{\mathcal{B}}$, how can we recover the vector $\mathbf{x}$?

c. If we are given the vector $\mathbf{x}$, how can we find $\{\mathbf{x}\}_{\mathcal{B}}$?

d. Suppose that

$$\mathcal{B} = \left\{ \begin{bmatrix} 1 \\ 3 \end{bmatrix}, \begin{bmatrix} 1 \\ 1 \end{bmatrix} \right\}$$

is a basis for $\mathbb{R}^2$. If $\{\mathbf{x}\}_{\mathcal{B}} = \begin{bmatrix} 1 \\ -2 \end{bmatrix}$, find the vector $\mathbf{x}$.

e. If $\mathbf{x} = \begin{bmatrix} 2 \\ -4 \end{bmatrix}$, find $\{\mathbf{x}\}_{\mathcal{B}}$.

Activity 3.3.2 This activity investigates these two color models, which we view as coordinate systems for describing colors.

a. First, we will explore the RGB color model.

   There is an interactive diagram, available at the top of the page `gvsu.edu/s/0Jc`, that accompanies this activity.

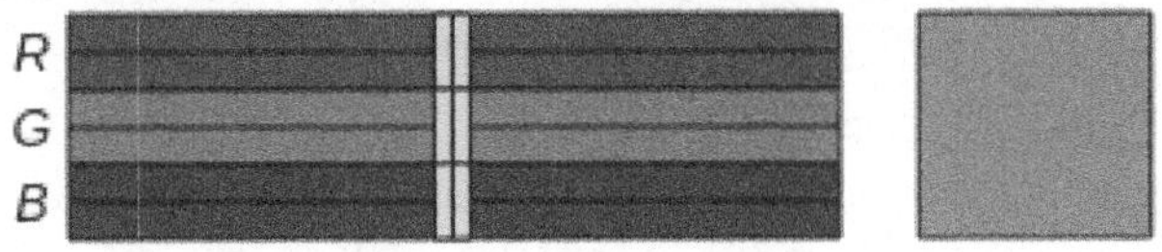

Figure 3.3.2 The RGB color model.

   1. What happens when $G = 0$, $B = 0$ (pushed all the way to the left), and R is allowed to vary?
   2. What happens when $R = 0$, $G = 0$, and B is allowed to vary?
   3. How can you create black in this color model?
   4. How can you create white?

b. Next, we will explore the YC_bC_r color model.

   There is an interactive diagram, available in the middle of the page `gvsu.edu/s/0Jc`, that accompanies this activity.

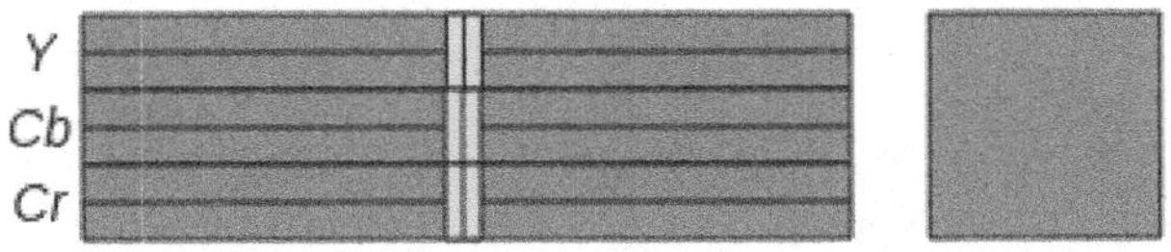

Figure 3.3.3 The YC_bC_r color model.

   1. What happens when $C_b = 0$ and $C_r = 0$ (kept in the center) and Y is allowed to vary?
   2. What happens when $Y = 0$ (pushed to the left), $C_r = 0$ (kept in the center), and C_b is allowed to increase between 0 and 127.5?
   3. What happens when $Y = 0$, $C_b = 0$, and C_r is allowed to increase between 0 and 127.5?
   4. How can you create black in this color model?
   5. How can you create white?

c. Verify that $\mathcal{B}$ is a basis for $\mathbb{R}^3$.

d. Find the matrix $P_{\mathcal{B}}$ that converts from $\begin{bmatrix} Y \\ C_b \\ C_r \end{bmatrix}$ coordinates into $\begin{bmatrix} R \\ G \\ B \end{bmatrix}$ coordinates. Then find the matrix $P_{\mathcal{B}}^{-1}$ that converts from $\begin{bmatrix} R \\ G \\ B \end{bmatrix}$ coordinates back into $\begin{bmatrix} Y \\ C_b \\ C_r \end{bmatrix}$ coordinates.

e. Find the $\begin{bmatrix} Y \\ C_b \\ C_r \end{bmatrix}$ coordinates for the following colors and check, using the diagrams above, that the two representations agree.

   1. Pure red is $\begin{bmatrix} R \\ G \\ B \end{bmatrix} = \begin{bmatrix} 255 \\ 0 \\ 0 \end{bmatrix}$.

2. Pure blue is $\begin{bmatrix} R \\ G \\ B \end{bmatrix} = \begin{bmatrix} 0 \\ 0 \\ 255 \end{bmatrix}$.

3. Pure white is $\begin{bmatrix} R \\ G \\ B \end{bmatrix} = \begin{bmatrix} 255 \\ 255 \\ 255 \end{bmatrix}$.

4. Pure black is $\begin{bmatrix} R \\ G \\ B \end{bmatrix} = \begin{bmatrix} 0 \\ 0 \\ 0 \end{bmatrix}$.

f. Find the $\begin{bmatrix} R \\ G \\ B \end{bmatrix}$ coordinates for the following colors and check, using the diagrams above, that the two representations agree.

1. $\begin{bmatrix} Y \\ C_b \\ C_r \end{bmatrix} = \begin{bmatrix} 128 \\ 0 \\ 0 \end{bmatrix}$.

2. $\begin{bmatrix} Y \\ C_b \\ C_r \end{bmatrix} = \begin{bmatrix} 128 \\ 60 \\ 0 \end{bmatrix}$.

3. $\begin{bmatrix} Y \\ C_b \\ C_r \end{bmatrix} = \begin{bmatrix} 128 \\ 0 \\ 60 \end{bmatrix}$.

g. Write an expression for

1. The luminance Y as it depends on R, G, and B.
2. The blue chrominance C_b as it depends on R, G, and B.
3. The red chrominance C_r as it depends on R, G, and B.

Explain how these quantities can be roughly interpreted by stating that

1. the luminance represents the brightness of the color.
2. the blue chrominance measures the amount of blue in the color.
3. the red chrominance measures the amount of red in the color.

Activity 3.3.3 We will explore the influence that the Fourier coefficients have on the vector **x**.

a. To begin, we'll look at the Fourier coefficient F_0.

There is an interactive diagram that accompanies this part of the activity and that is available at the top of `gvsu.edu/s/0Jd`.

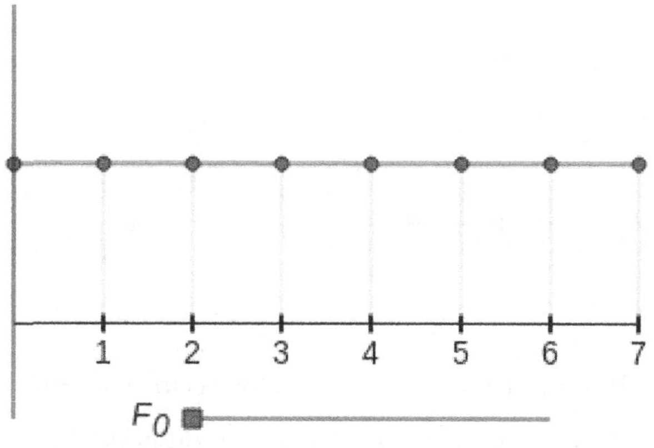

Figure 3.3.10 The effect of the Fourier coefficient F_0 on the vector $\mathbf{x} = F_0\mathbf{v}_0$.

Describe the effect that F_0 has on the vector **x**. Would you describe the components in **x** as constant, slowly varying, or rapidly varying?

b. By comparison, let's see how the Fourier coefficient F_3 influences **x**.

There is an interactive diagram that accompanies this part of the activity and that is available in the middle of `gvsu.edu/s/0Jd`.

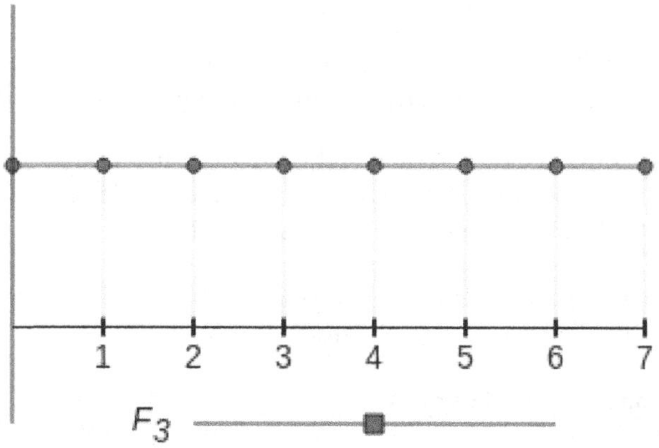

Figure 3.3.11 The effect of the Fourier coefficient F_3 on the vector $\mathbf{x} = F_3\mathbf{v}_3$.

Describe the effect that F_3 has on the vector **x**. Would you describe the components in **x** as constant, slowly varying, or rapidly varying?

c. Let's now investigate how the Fourier coefficient F_7 influences the vector **x**.

There is an interactive diagram that accompanies this part of the activity and that is available at the bottom of `gvsu.edu/s/0Jd`.

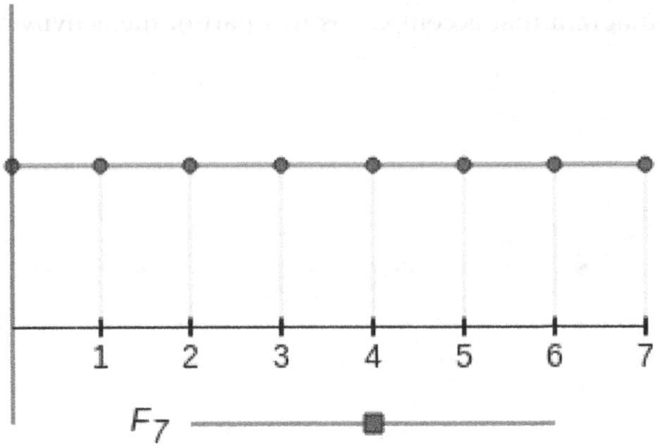

Figure 3.3.12 The effect of the Fourier coefficient F_0 on the vector $\mathbf{x} = F_7\mathbf{v}_7$.

Describe the effect that F_7 has on the vector $\mathbf{x}$. Would you describe the components in $\mathbf{x}$ as constant, slowly varying, or rapidly varying?

d. If the components of $\mathbf{x}$ vary relatively slowly, what would you expect to be true of the Fourier coefficients F_j?

e. The Sage cell below will construct the vector $P_{\mathcal{B}}$, which is denoted `P`, and its inverse $P_{\mathcal{B}}^{-1}$, which is denoted `Pinv`. Evaluate this Sage cell and notice that it prints the matrix $P_{\mathcal{B}}^{-1}$.

```
mat = [[cos((2*i+1)*j*pi/16) for j in range(8)] for i in range(8)]
P = matrix(mat).numerical_approx()
Pinv = P.inverse()
print (Pinv.numerical_approx(digits=3))
```

Now look at the form of $P_{\mathcal{B}}^{-1}$ and explain why F_0 is the average of the luminance values in the vector $\mathbf{x}$.

f. The Sage cell below defines the vector $\mathbf{x}$, which is the vector of luminance values in the first column, as seen in Figure 3.3.8. Use the cell below to find the vector $\mathbf{f}$ of Fourier coefficients $F_0, F_1, \ldots, F_7$. If you have evaluated the cell above, you will still be able to refer to `P` and `Pinv` in this cell.

```
x = vector([176,181,165,139,131,131,140,150])
#  find the vector of Fourier coefficients f below
f =
print (f.numerical_approx(digits=4))
```

Write the Fourier coefficients and discuss the relative sizes of the coefficients.

g. Let's see what happens when we simply ignore the coefficients F_6 and F_7. Form a new vector of Fourier coefficients by rounding the coefficients to the nearest integer and setting F_6 and F_7 to zero. This is an approximation to $\mathbf{f}$, the vector of Fourier coefficients. Use the approximation to $\mathbf{f}$ to form an approximation of the vector $\mathbf{x}$.

```
# define fapprox below and then find xapprox
fapprox =
xapprox =
print ("x␣␣␣␣␣␣␣=", x)
print ("xapprox=", xapprox.numerical_approx(digits=3))
```

How much does your approximation differ from the actual vector $\mathbf{x}$?

h. When we ignore the Fourier coefficients corresponding to rapidly varying basis elements, we see that the vector $\mathbf{x}$ that we reconstruct is very close to the original one. In fact, the luminance values in the approximation differ by at most one or two from the actual luminance values. Our eyes are not sensitive enough to detect this difference.

So far, we have concentrated on only one column in our 8×8 block of luminance values. Let's now consider all of the columns. The following Sage cell defines a matrix called `luminance`, which is the 8×8 matrix of luminance values. Find the 8×8 matrix F whose columns are the Fourier coefficients of the columns of luminance values.

```
luminance = matrix(8,8, [176, 170, 170, 169, 162, 160, 155, 150, 181,
179, 175, 167, 162, 160, 154, 149, 165, 170, 169, 161, 162, 161, 160,
158, 139, 150, 164, 166, 159, 160, 162, 163, 131, 137, 157, 165, 163,
163, 164, 164, 131, 132, 153, 161, 167, 167, 167, 169, 140, 142, 157,
166, 166, 166, 167, 169, 150, 152, 160, 168, 172, 170, 168, 168])
# define your matrix F below
F =
print (F.numerical_approx(digits=3))
```

i. Notice that the first row of this matrix consists of the Fourier coefficient F_0 for each of the columns. Just as we saw before, the entries in this row do not change significantly as we move across the row. In the Sage cell below, write these entries in the vector **y** and find the corresponding Fourier coefficients.

```
# define the vector y as the entries in the first row of F
y =
y_fourier =
print (y_fourier.numerical_approx(digits=3))
```

3.4 Determinants

Preview Activity 3.4.1 We will explore the area formula in this preview activity.

a. Find the area of the following parallelograms.

1.

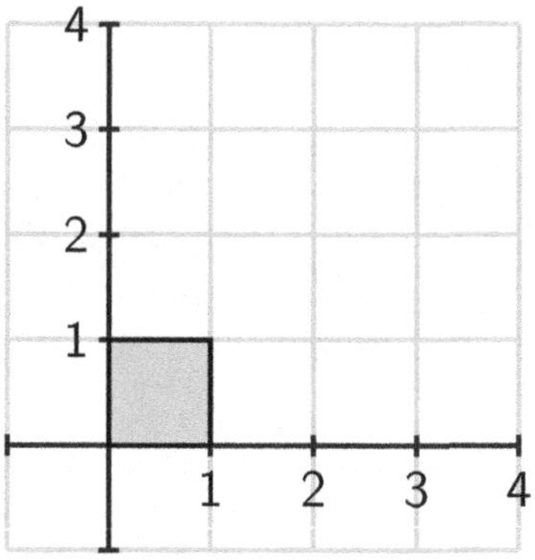

2.

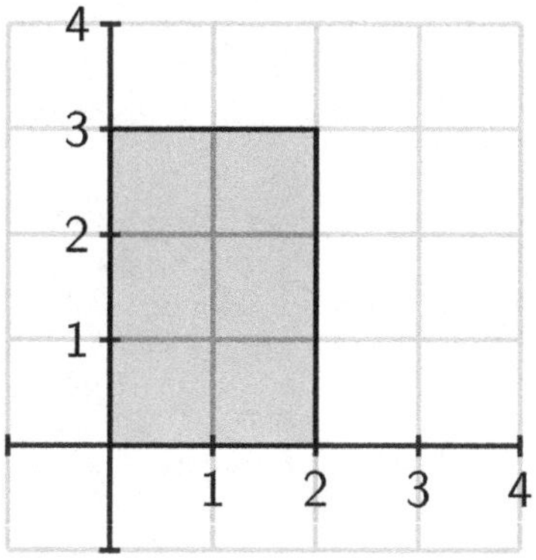

3.

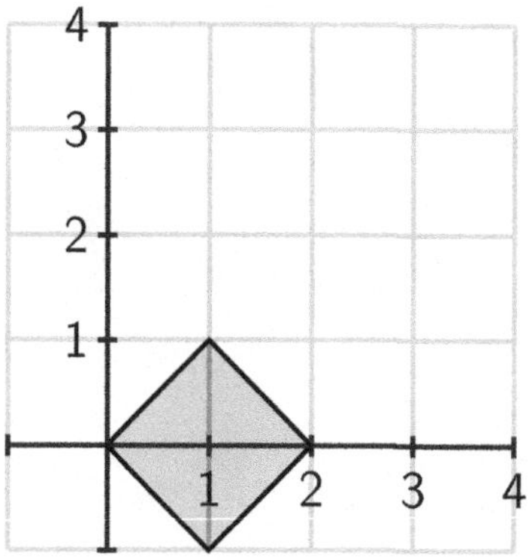

4.

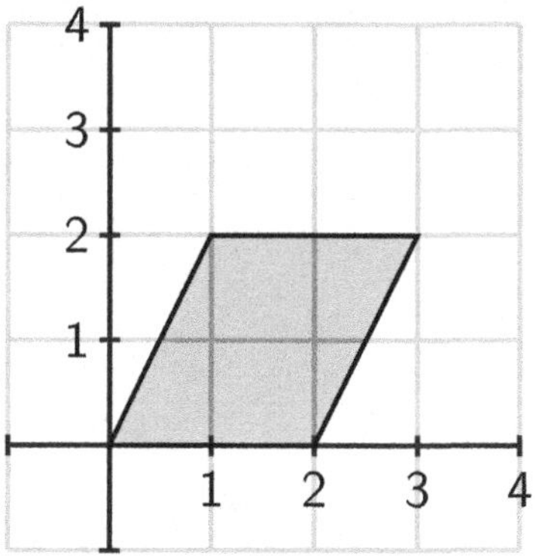

5.

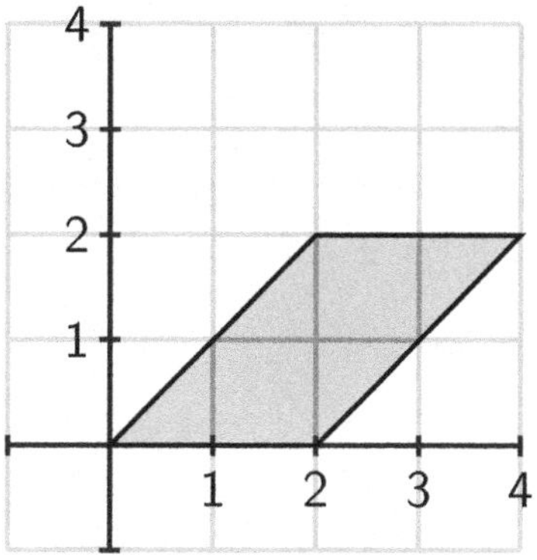

b. Explain why the area of the parallelogram formed by the vectors $\mathbf{v}$ and $\mathbf{w}_1$ is the same as that formed by $\mathbf{v}$ and $\mathbf{w}_2$.

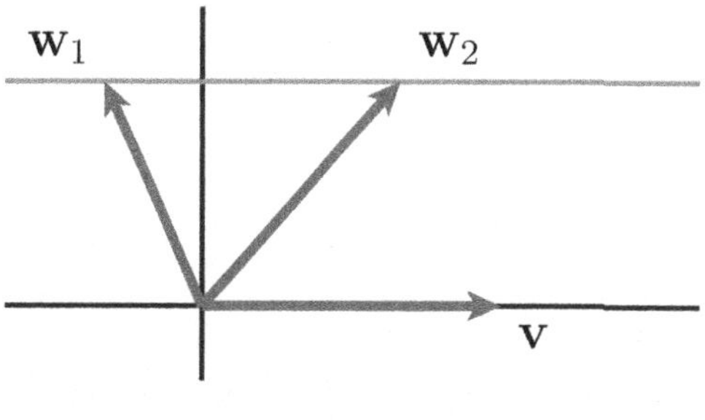

3.4 Determinants

Activity 3.4.2 In this activity, we will find the determinant of some simple 2×2 matrices and discover some important properties of determinants.

There is an interactive diagram at `gvsu.edu/s/0J9` that accompanies this activity.

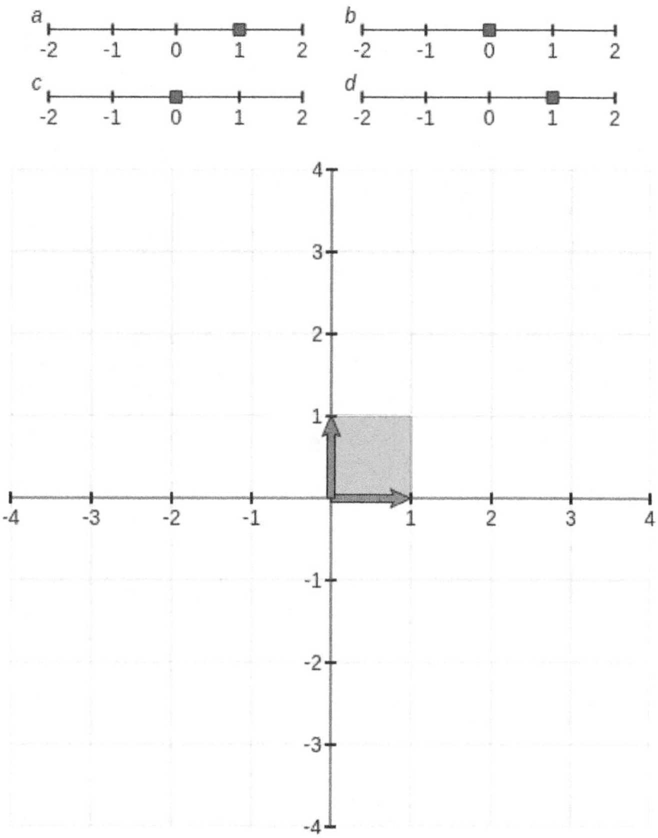

Figure 3.4.6 The geometric meaning of the determinant of a matrix.

a. Use the diagram to find the determinant of the matrix $\begin{bmatrix} -\frac{1}{2} & 0 \\ 0 & 2 \end{bmatrix}$. Along with Example 3.4.4, what does this lead you to believe is generally true about the determinant of a diagonal matrix?

b. Use the diagram to find the determinant of the matrix $\begin{bmatrix} 0 & 1 \\ 1 & 0 \end{bmatrix}$. What is the geometric effect of the matrix transformation defined by this matrix?

c. Use the diagram to find the determinant of the matrix $\begin{bmatrix} 2 & 1 \\ 0 & 1 \end{bmatrix}$. More generally, what do you notice about the determinant of any matrix of the form $\begin{bmatrix} 2 & k \\ 0 & 1 \end{bmatrix}$? What does this say about the determinant of an upper triangular matrix?

d. Use the diagram to find the determinant of any matrix of the form $\begin{bmatrix} 2 & 0 \\ k & 1 \end{bmatrix}$. What does this say about the determinant of a lower triangular matrix?

e. Use the diagram to find the determinant of the matrix $\begin{bmatrix} 1 & -1 \\ -2 & 2 \end{bmatrix}$. In general, what is the determinant of a matrix whose columns are linearly dependent?

f. Consider the matrices

$$A = \begin{bmatrix} 2 & 1 \\ 2 & -1 \end{bmatrix}, \quad B = \begin{bmatrix} 1 & 0 \\ 0 & 2 \end{bmatrix}.$$

Use the diagram to find the determinants of A, B, and AB. What does this suggest is generally true about the relationship of $\det(AB)$ to $\det(A)$ and $\det(B)$?

Activity 3.4.3 We will investigate the connection between the determinant of a matrix and its invertibility using Gaussian elimination.

a. Consider the two upper triangular matrices

$$U_1 = \begin{bmatrix} 1 & -1 & 2 \\ 0 & 2 & 4 \\ 0 & 0 & -2 \end{bmatrix}, \quad U_2 = \begin{bmatrix} 1 & -1 & 2 \\ 0 & 2 & 4 \\ 0 & 0 & 0 \end{bmatrix}.$$

Remembering Proposition 3.1.9, which of the matrices U_1 and U_2 are invertible? What are the determinants $\det(U_1)$ and $\det(U_2)$?

b. Explain why an upper triangular matrix is invertible if and only if its determinant is not zero.

c. Let's now consider the matrix

$$A = \begin{bmatrix} 1 & -1 & 2 \\ -2 & 2 & -6 \\ 3 & -1 & 10 \end{bmatrix}$$

and begin the Gaussian elimination process with a row replacement operation

$$A = \begin{bmatrix} 1 & -1 & 2 \\ -2 & 2 & -6 \\ 3 & -1 & 10 \end{bmatrix} \sim \begin{bmatrix} 1 & -1 & 2 \\ 0 & 0 & -2 \\ 3 & -1 & 10 \end{bmatrix} = A_1.$$

What is the relationship between $\det(A)$ and $\det(A_1)$?

d. Next we perform another row replacement operation:

$$A_1 = \begin{bmatrix} 1 & -1 & 2 \\ 0 & 0 & -2 \\ 3 & -1 & 10 \end{bmatrix} \sim \begin{bmatrix} 1 & -1 & 2 \\ 0 & 0 & -2 \\ 0 & 2 & 4 \end{bmatrix} = A_2.$$

What is the relationship between $\det(A)$ and $\det(A_2)$?

e. Finally, we perform an interchange:

$$A_2 = \begin{bmatrix} 1 & -1 & 2 \\ 0 & 0 & -2 \\ 0 & 2 & 4 \end{bmatrix} \sim \begin{bmatrix} 1 & -1 & 2 \\ 0 & 2 & 4 \\ 0 & 0 & -2 \end{bmatrix} = U$$

to arrive at an upper triangular matrix U. What is the relationship between $\det(A)$ and $\det(U)$?

f. Since U is upper triangular, we can compute its determinant, which allows us to find $\det(A)$. What is $\det(A)$? Is A invertible?

g. Now consider the matrix

$$A = \begin{bmatrix} 1 & -1 & 3 \\ 0 & 2 & -2 \\ 2 & 1 & 3 \end{bmatrix}.$$

Perform a sequence of row operations to find an upper triangular matrix U that is row equivalent to A. Use this to determine $\det(A)$ and whether A is invertible?

h. Suppose we apply a sequence of row operations on a matrix A to obtain A'. Explain why $\det(A) \neq 0$ if and only if $\det(A') \neq 0$.

i. Explain why an $n \times n$ matrix A is invertible if and only if $\det(A) \neq 0$.

Activity 3.4.4 We will explore cofactor expansions through some examples.

a. Using a cofactor expansion, show that the determinant of the following matrix

$$\det\begin{bmatrix} 2 & 0 & -1 \\ 3 & 1 & 2 \\ -2 & 4 & -3 \end{bmatrix} = -36.$$

Remember that you can choose any row or column to create the expansion, but the choice of a particular row or column may simplify the computation.

b. Use a cofactor expansion to find the determinant of

$$\begin{bmatrix} -3 & 0 & 0 & 0 \\ 4 & 1 & 0 & 0 \\ -1 & 4 & -4 & 0 \\ 0 & 3 & 2 & 3 \end{bmatrix}.$$

Explain how the cofactor expansion technique shows that the determinant of a triangular matrix is equal to the product of its diagonal entries.

c. Use a cofactor expansion to determine whether the following vectors form a basis of $\mathbb{R}^3$:

$$\begin{bmatrix} 2 \\ -1 \\ -2 \end{bmatrix}, \begin{bmatrix} 1 \\ -1 \\ 2 \end{bmatrix}, \begin{bmatrix} 1 \\ 0 \\ -4 \end{bmatrix}.$$

d. Sage will compute the determinant of a matrix `A` with the command `A.det()`. Use Sage to find the determinant of the matrix

$$\begin{bmatrix} 2 & 1 & -2 & -3 \\ 3 & 0 & -1 & -2 \\ -3 & 4 & 1 & 2 \\ 1 & 3 & 3 & -1 \end{bmatrix}.$$

3.5 Subspaces

Preview Activity 3.5.1 Let's consider the following matrix A and its reduced row echelon form.

$$A = \begin{bmatrix} 2 & -1 & 2 & 3 \\ 1 & 0 & 0 & 2 \\ -2 & 2 & -4 & -2 \end{bmatrix} \sim \begin{bmatrix} 1 & 0 & 0 & 2 \\ 0 & 1 & -2 & 1 \\ 0 & 0 & 0 & 0 \end{bmatrix}.$$

a. Are the columns of A linearly independent? Is the span of the columns $\mathbb{R}^3$?

b. Give a parametric description of the solution space to the homogeneous equation $A\mathbf{x} = \mathbf{0}$.

c. Explain how this parametric description produces two vectors $\mathbf{w}_1$ and $\mathbf{w}_2$ whose span is the solution space to the equation $A\mathbf{x} = \mathbf{0}$.

d. What can you say about the linear independence of the set of vectors $\mathbf{w}_1$ and $\mathbf{w}_2$?

e. Let's denote the columns of A as $\mathbf{v}_1, \mathbf{v}_2, \mathbf{v}_3$, and $\mathbf{v}_4$. Explain why $\mathbf{v}_3$ and $\mathbf{v}_4$ can be written as linear combinations of $\mathbf{v}_1$ and $\mathbf{v}_2$.

f. Explain why $\mathbf{v}_1$ and $\mathbf{v}_2$ are linearly independent and $\text{Span}\{\mathbf{v}_1, \mathbf{v}_2\} = \text{Span}\{\mathbf{v}_1, \mathbf{v}_2, \mathbf{v}_3, \mathbf{v}_4\}$.

Activity 3.5.2 We will look at some sets of vectors and the subspaces they form.

a. If $\mathbf{v}_1, \mathbf{v}_2, \ldots, \mathbf{v}_n$ is a set of vectors in $\mathbb{R}^m$, explain why $\mathbf{0}$ can be expressed as a linear combination of these vectors. Use this fact to explain why the zero vector $\mathbf{0}$ belongs to any subspace in $\mathbb{R}^m$.

b. Explain why the line on the left of Figure 3.5.3 is not a subspace of $\mathbb{R}^2$ and why the line on the right is.

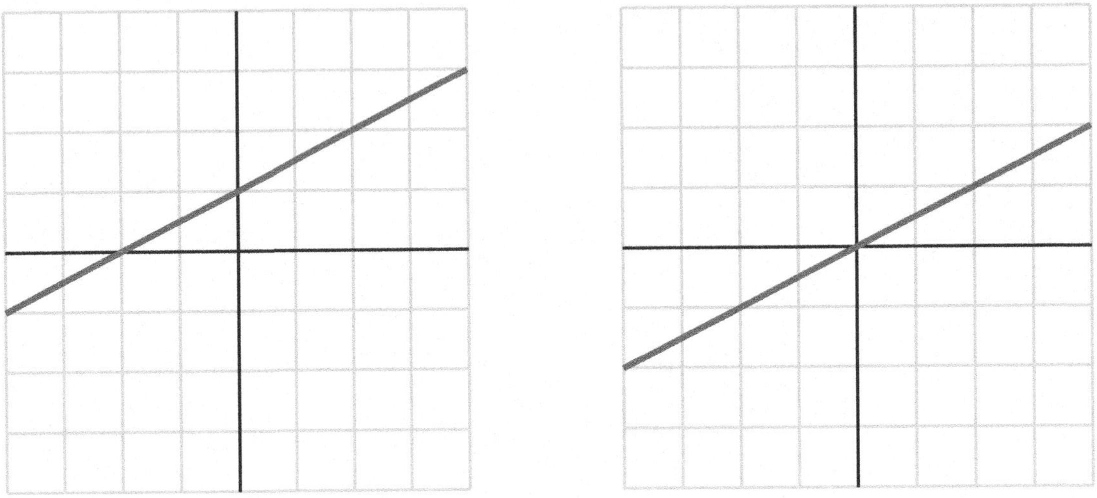

Figure 3.5.3 Two lines in $\mathbb{R}^2$, one of which is a subspace and one of which is not.

c. Consider the vectors

$$\mathbf{v}_1 = \begin{bmatrix} 1 \\ 0 \\ 1 \end{bmatrix}, \quad \mathbf{v}_2 = \begin{bmatrix} 0 \\ 1 \\ 1 \end{bmatrix}, \quad \mathbf{v}_3 = \begin{bmatrix} 1 \\ 1 \\ 0 \end{bmatrix},$$

and describe the subspace $S = \text{Span}\{\mathbf{v}_1, \mathbf{v}_2, \mathbf{v}_3\}$ of $\mathbb{R}^3$.

d. Consider the vectors

$$\mathbf{w}_1 = \begin{bmatrix} 2 \\ 1 \\ 0 \end{bmatrix}, \quad \mathbf{w}_2 = \begin{bmatrix} -1 \\ 1 \\ -1 \end{bmatrix}, \quad \mathbf{w}_3 = \begin{bmatrix} 0 \\ 3 \\ -2 \end{bmatrix}$$

1. Write $\mathbf{w}_3$ as a linear combination of $\mathbf{w}_1$ and $\mathbf{w}_2$.
2. Explain why $\text{Span}\{\mathbf{w}_1, \mathbf{w}_2, \mathbf{w}_3\} = \text{Span}\{\mathbf{w}_1, \mathbf{w}_2\}$.
3. Describe the subspace $S = \text{Span}\{\mathbf{w}_1, \mathbf{w}_2, \mathbf{w}_3\}$ of $\mathbb{R}^3$.

e. Suppose that $\mathbf{v}_1$, $\mathbf{v}_2$, $\mathbf{v}_3$, and $\mathbf{v}_4$ are four vectors in $\mathbb{R}^3$ and that

$$\begin{bmatrix} \mathbf{v}_1 & \mathbf{v}_2 & \mathbf{v}_3 & \mathbf{v}_4 \end{bmatrix} \sim \begin{bmatrix} 1 & 2 & 0 & -2 \\ 0 & 0 & 1 & 1 \\ 0 & 0 & 0 & 0 \end{bmatrix}.$$

Give a description of the subspace $S = \text{Span}\{\mathbf{v}_1, \mathbf{v}_2, \mathbf{v}_3, \mathbf{v}_4\}$ of $\mathbb{R}^3$.

Activity 3.5.3 We will explore some column spaces in this activity.

a. Consider the matrix

$$A = \begin{bmatrix} \mathbf{v}_1 & \mathbf{v}_2 & \mathbf{v}_3 \end{bmatrix} = \begin{bmatrix} 1 & 3 & -1 \\ -2 & 0 & -4 \\ 1 & 2 & 0 \end{bmatrix}.$$

Since $\text{Col}(A)$ is the span of the columns, we have

$$\text{Col}(A) = \text{Span}\{\mathbf{v}_1, \mathbf{v}_2, \mathbf{v}_3\}.$$

Explain why $\mathbf{v}_3$ can be written as a linear combination of $\mathbf{v}_1$ and $\mathbf{v}_2$ and why $\text{Col}(A) = \text{Span}\{\mathbf{v}_1, \mathbf{v}_2\}$.

b. Explain why the vectors $\mathbf{v}_1$ and $\mathbf{v}_2$ form a basis for $\text{Col}(A)$ and why $\text{Col}(A)$ is a 2-dimensional subspace of $\mathbb{R}^3$ and therefore a plane.

c. Now consider the matrix B and its reduced row echelon form:

$$B = \begin{bmatrix} -2 & -4 & 0 & 6 \\ 1 & 2 & 0 & -3 \end{bmatrix} \sim \begin{bmatrix} 1 & 2 & 0 & -3 \\ 0 & 0 & 0 & 0 \end{bmatrix}.$$

Explain why $\text{Col}(B)$ is a 1-dimensional subspace of $\mathbb{R}^2$ and is therefore a line.

d. For a general matrix A, what is the relationship between the dimension $\dim \text{Col}(A)$ and the number of pivot positions in A?

e. How does the location of the pivot positions indicate a basis for $\text{Col}(A)$?

f. If A is an invertible 9×9 matrix, what can you say about the column space $\text{Col}(A)$?

g. Suppose that A is an 8×10 matrix and that $\text{Col}(A) = \mathbb{R}^8$. If $\mathbf{b}$ is an 8-dimensional vector, what can you say about the equation $A\mathbf{x} = \mathbf{b}$?

Activity 3.5.4 We will explore some null spaces in this activity and see why Nul(A) satisfies the definition of a subspace.

a. Consider the matrix

$$A = \begin{bmatrix} 1 & 3 & -1 & 2 \\ -2 & 0 & -4 & 2 \\ 1 & 2 & 0 & 1 \end{bmatrix}$$

and give a parametric description of the solution space to the equation $A\mathbf{x} = \mathbf{0}$. In other words, give a parametric description of Nul(A).

b. This parametric description shows that the vectors satisfying the equation $A\mathbf{x} = \mathbf{0}$ can be written as a linear combination of a set of vectors. In other words, this description shows why Nul(A) is the span of a set of vectors and is therefore a subspace. Identify a set of vectors whose span is Nul(A).

c. Use this set of vectors to find a basis for Nul(A) and state the dimension of Nul(A).

d. The null space Nul(A) is a subspace of $\mathbb{R}^p$ for which value of p?

e. Now consider the matrix B whose reduced row echelon form is given by

$$B \sim \begin{bmatrix} 1 & 2 & 0 & -3 \\ 0 & 0 & 0 & 0 \end{bmatrix}.$$

Give a parametric description of Nul(B).

f. The parametric description gives a set of vectors that span Nul(B). Explain why this set of vectors is linearly independent and hence forms a basis. What is the dimension of Nul(B)?

g. For a general matrix A, how does the number of pivot positions indicate the dimension of Nul(A)?

h. Suppose that the columns of a matrix A are linearly independent. What can you say about Nul(A)?

4 Eigenvalues and eigenvectors

4.1 An introduction to eigenvalues and eigenvectors

Preview Activity 4.1.1 Before we introduce the definition of eigenvectors and eigenvalues, it will be helpful to remember some ideas we have seen previously.

a. Suppose that $\mathbf{v}$ is the vector shown in the figure. Sketch the vector $2\mathbf{v}$ and the vector $-\mathbf{v}$.

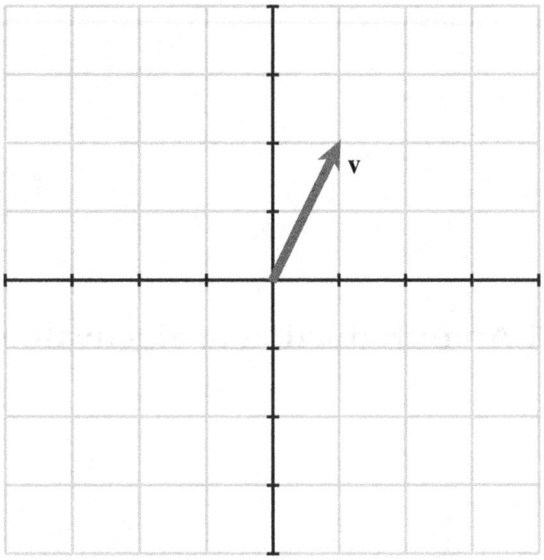

b. State the geometric effect that scalar multiplication has on the vector $\mathbf{v}$. Then sketch all the vectors of the form $\lambda\mathbf{v}$ where λ is a scalar.

c. State the geometric effect of the matrix transformation defined by

$$\begin{bmatrix} 3 & 0 \\ 0 & -1 \end{bmatrix}.$$

d. Suppose that A is a 2×2 matrix and that $\mathbf{v}_1$ and $\mathbf{v}_2$ are vectors such that

$$A\mathbf{v}_1 = 3\mathbf{v}_1, \qquad A\mathbf{v}_2 = -\mathbf{v}_2.$$

Use the linearity of matrix multiplication to express the following vectors in terms of $\mathbf{v}_1$ and $\mathbf{v}_2$.

1. $A(4\mathbf{v}_1)$.
2. $A(\mathbf{v}_1 + \mathbf{v}_2)$.
3. $A(4\mathbf{v}_1 - 3\mathbf{v}_2)$.
4. $A^2\mathbf{v}_1$.
5. $A^2(4\mathbf{v}_1 - 3\mathbf{v}_2)$.
6. $A^4\mathbf{v}_1$.

Activity 4.1.2 This definition has an important geometric interpretation that we will investigate here.

a. Suppose that $\mathbf{v}$ is a nonzero vector and that λ is a scalar. What is the geometric relationship between $\mathbf{v}$ and $\lambda\mathbf{v}$?

b. Let's now consider the eigenvector condition: $A\mathbf{v} = \lambda\mathbf{v}$. Here we have two vectors, $\mathbf{v}$ and $A\mathbf{v}$. If $A\mathbf{v} = \lambda\mathbf{v}$, what is the geometric relationship between $\mathbf{v}$ and $A\mathbf{v}$?

c. There is an interactive diagram, available at `gvsu.edu/s/0Ja`, that accompanies this activity.

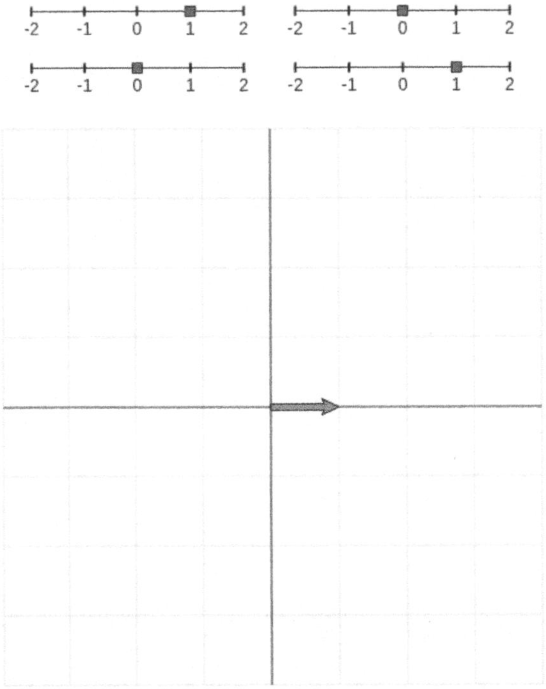

Figure 4.1.3 A geometric interpretation of the eigenvalue-eigenvector condition $A\mathbf{v} = \lambda\mathbf{v}$.

Choose the matrix $A = \begin{bmatrix} 1 & 2 \\ 2 & 1 \end{bmatrix}$. Move the vector $\mathbf{v}$ so that the eigenvector condition holds. What is the eigenvector $\mathbf{v}$ and what is the associated eigenvalue?

d. By algebraically computing $A\mathbf{v}$, verify that the eigenvector condition holds for the vector $\mathbf{v}$ that you found.

e. If you multiply the eigenvector $\mathbf{v}$ that you found by 2, do you still have an eigenvector? If so, what is the associated eigenvalue?

f. Are you able to find another eigenvector $\mathbf{v}$ that is not a scalar multiple of the first one that you found? If so, what is the eigenvector and what is the associated eigenvalue?

g. Now consider the matrix $A = \begin{bmatrix} 2 & 1 \\ 0 & 2 \end{bmatrix}$. Use the diagram to describe any eigenvectors and associated eigenvalues.

h. Finally, consider the matrix $A = \begin{bmatrix} 0 & -1 \\ 1 & 0 \end{bmatrix}$. Use the diagram to describe any eigenvectors and associated eigenvalues. What geometric transformation does this matrix perform on vectors? How does this explain the presence of any eigenvectors?

Activity 4.1.3 Let's consider an example that illustrates how we can put these ideas to use.

Suppose that we work for a car rental company that has two locations, P and Q. When a customer rents a car at one location, they have the option to return it to either location at the end of the day. After doing some market research, we determine:

- 80% of the cars rented at location P are returned to P and 20% are returned to Q.
- 40% of the cars rented at location Q are returned to Q and 60% are returned to P.

a. Suppose that there are 1000 cars at location P and no cars at location Q on Monday morning. How many cars are there are locations P and Q at the end of the day on Monday?

b. How many are at locations P and Q at end of the day on Tuesday?

c. If we let P_k and Q_k be the number of cars at locations P and Q, respectively, at the end of day k, we then have

$$\begin{aligned} P_{k+1} &= 0.8P_k + 0.6Q_k \\ Q_{k+1} &= 0.2P_k + 0.4Q_k. \end{aligned}$$

We can write the vector $\mathbf{x}_k = \begin{bmatrix} P_k \\ Q_k \end{bmatrix}$ to reflect the number of cars at the two locations at the end of day k, which says that

$$\mathbf{x}_{k+1} = \begin{bmatrix} 0.8 & 0.6 \\ 0.2 & 0.4 \end{bmatrix} \mathbf{x}_k$$

or $\mathbf{x}_{k+1} = A\mathbf{x}_k$ where $A = \begin{bmatrix} 0.8 & 0.6 \\ 0.2 & 0.4 \end{bmatrix}$.

Suppose that

$$\mathbf{v}_1 = \begin{bmatrix} 3 \\ 1 \end{bmatrix}, \quad \mathbf{v}_2 = \begin{bmatrix} -1 \\ 1 \end{bmatrix}.$$

Compute $A\mathbf{v}_1$ and $A\mathbf{v}_2$ to demonstrate that $\mathbf{v}_1$ and $\mathbf{v}_2$ are eigenvectors of A. What are the associated eigenvalues λ_1 and λ_2?

d. We said that 1000 cars are initially at location P and none at location Q. This means that the initial vector describing the number of cars is $\mathbf{x}_0 = \begin{bmatrix} 1000 \\ 0 \end{bmatrix}$. Write $\mathbf{x}_0$ as a linear combination of $\mathbf{v}_1$ and $\mathbf{v}_2$.

e. Remember that $\mathbf{v}_1$ and $\mathbf{v}_2$ are eigenvectors of A. Use the linearity of matrix multiplication to write the vector $\mathbf{x}_1 = A\mathbf{x}_0$, describing the number of cars at the two locations at the end of the first day, as a linear combination of $\mathbf{v}_1$ and $\mathbf{v}_2$.

f. Write the vector $\mathbf{x}_2 = A\mathbf{x}_1$ as a linear combination of $\mathbf{v}_1$ and $\mathbf{v}_2$. Then write the next few vectors as linear combinations of $\mathbf{v}_1$ and $\mathbf{v}_2$:

   1. $\mathbf{x}_3 = A\mathbf{x}_2$.
   2. $\mathbf{x}_4 = A\mathbf{x}_3$.
   3. $\mathbf{x}_5 = A\mathbf{x}_4$.
   4. $\mathbf{x}_6 = A\mathbf{x}_5$.

g. What will happen to the number of cars at the two locations after a very long time? Explain how writing $\mathbf{x}_0$ as a linear combination of eigenvectors helps you determine the long-term behavior.

4.2 Finding eigenvalues and eigenvectors

Preview Activity 4.2.1 Let's begin by reviewing some important ideas that we have seen previously.

a. Suppose that A is a square matrix and that the nonzero vector $\mathbf{x}$ is a solution to the homogeneous equation $A\mathbf{x} = \mathbf{0}$. What can we conclude about the invertibility of A?

b. How does the determinant $\det(A)$ tell us if there is a nonzero solution to the homogeneous equation $A\mathbf{x} = \mathbf{0}$?

c. Suppose that

$$A = \begin{bmatrix} 3 & -1 & 1 \\ 0 & 2 & 4 \\ 1 & 1 & 3 \end{bmatrix}.$$

Find the determinant $\det(A)$. What does this tell us about the solution space to the homogeneous equation $A\mathbf{x} = \mathbf{0}$?

d. Find a basis for $\text{Nul}(A)$.

e. What is the relationship between the rank of a matrix and the dimension of its null space?

Activity 4.2.2 The eigenvalues of a square matrix are defined by the condition that there be a nonzero solution to the homogeneous equation $(A - \lambda I)\mathbf{v} = \mathbf{0}$.

a. If there is a nonzero solution to the homogeneous equation $(A - \lambda I)\mathbf{v} = \mathbf{0}$, what can we conclude about the invertibility of the matrix $A - \lambda I$?

b. If there is a nonzero solution to the homogeneous equation $(A - \lambda I)\mathbf{v} = \mathbf{0}$, what can we conclude about the determinant $\det(A - \lambda I)$?

c. Let's consider the matrix

$$A = \begin{bmatrix} 1 & 2 \\ 2 & 1 \end{bmatrix}$$

from which we construct

$$A - \lambda I = \begin{bmatrix} 1 & 2 \\ 2 & 1 \end{bmatrix} - \lambda \begin{bmatrix} 1 & 0 \\ 0 & 1 \end{bmatrix} = \begin{bmatrix} 1-\lambda & 2 \\ 2 & 1-\lambda \end{bmatrix}.$$

Find the determinant $\det(A - \lambda I)$. What kind of equation do you obtain when we set this determinant to zero to obtain $\det(A - \lambda I) = 0$?

d. Use the determinant you found in the previous part to find the eigenvalues λ by solving the equation $\det(A - \lambda I) = 0$. We considered this matrix in Activity 4.1.2 so we should find the same eigenvalues for A that we found by reasoning geometrically there.

e. Consider the matrix $A = \begin{bmatrix} 2 & 1 \\ 0 & 2 \end{bmatrix}$ and find its eigenvalues by solving the equation $\det(A - \lambda I) = 0$.

f. Consider the matrix $A = \begin{bmatrix} 0 & -1 \\ 1 & 0 \end{bmatrix}$ and find its eigenvalues by solving the equation $\det(A - \lambda I) = 0$.

g. Find the eigenvalues of the triangular matrix $\begin{bmatrix} 3 & -1 & 4 \\ 0 & -2 & 3 \\ 0 & 0 & 1 \end{bmatrix}$. What is generally true about the eigenvalues of a triangular matrix?

Activity 4.2.3 In this activity, we will find the eigenvectors of a matrix as the null space of the matrix $A - \lambda I$.

a. Let's begin with the matrix $A = \begin{bmatrix} 1 & 2 \\ 2 & 1 \end{bmatrix}$. We have seen that $\lambda = 3$ is an eigenvalue. Form the matrix $A - 3I$ and find a basis for the eigenspace $E_3 = \text{Nul}(A - 3I)$. What is the dimension of this eigenspace? For each of the basis vectors $\mathbf{v}$, verify that $A\mathbf{v} = 3\mathbf{v}$.

b. We also saw that $\lambda = -1$ is an eigenvalue. Form the matrix $A - (-1)I$ and find a basis for the eigenspace E_{-1}. What is the dimension of this eigenspace? For each of the basis vectors $\mathbf{v}$, verify that $A\mathbf{v} = -\mathbf{v}$.

c. Is it possible to form a basis of $\mathbb{R}^2$ consisting of eigenvectors of A?

d. Now consider the matrix $A = \begin{bmatrix} 3 & 0 \\ 0 & 3 \end{bmatrix}$. Write the characteristic equation for A and use it to find the eigenvalues of A. For each eigenvalue, find a basis for its eigenspace E_λ. Is it possible to form a basis of $\mathbb{R}^2$ consisting of eigenvectors of A?

e. Next, consider the matrix $A = \begin{bmatrix} 2 & 1 \\ 0 & 2 \end{bmatrix}$. Write the characteristic equation for A and use it to find the eigenvalues of A. For each eigenvalue, find a basis for its eigenspace E_λ. Is it possible to form a basis of $\mathbb{R}^2$ consisting of eigenvectors of A?

f. Finally, find the eigenvalues and eigenvectors of the diagonal matrix $A = \begin{bmatrix} 4 & 0 \\ 0 & -1 \end{bmatrix}$. Explain your result by considering the geometric effect of the matrix transformation defined by A.

Activity 4.2.4

a. Identify the eigenvalues, and their multiplicities, of an $n \times n$ matrix whose characteristic polynomial is $(2-\lambda)^3(-3-\lambda)^{10}(5-\lambda)$. What can you conclude about the dimensions of the eigenspaces? What is the shape of the matrix? Do you have enough information to guarantee that there is a basis of $\mathbb{R}^n$ consisting of eigenvectors?

b. Find the eigenvalues of $\begin{bmatrix} 0 & -1 \\ 4 & -4 \end{bmatrix}$ and state their multiplicities. Can you find a basis of $\mathbb{R}^2$ consisting of eigenvectors of this matrix?

c. Consider the matrix $A = \begin{bmatrix} -1 & 0 & 2 \\ -2 & -2 & -4 \\ 0 & 0 & -2 \end{bmatrix}$ whose characteristic equation is

$$(-2-\lambda)^2(-1-\lambda) = 0.$$

1. Identify the eigenvalues and their multiplicities.
2. For each eigenvalue λ, find a basis of the eigenspace E_λ and state its dimension.
3. Is there a basis of $\mathbb{R}^3$ consisting of eigenvectors of A?

d. Now consider the matrix $A = \begin{bmatrix} -5 & -2 & -6 \\ -2 & -2 & -4 \\ 2 & 1 & 2 \end{bmatrix}$ whose characteristic equation is also

$$(-2-\lambda)^2(-1-\lambda) = 0.$$

1. Identify the eigenvalues and their multiplicities.
2. For each eigenvalue λ, find a basis of the eigenspace E_λ and state its dimension.
3. Is there a basis of $\mathbb{R}^3$ consisting of eigenvectors of A?

e. Consider the matrix $A = \begin{bmatrix} -5 & -2 & -6 \\ 4 & 1 & 8 \\ 2 & 1 & 2 \end{bmatrix}$ whose characteristic equation is

$$(-2-\lambda)(1-\lambda)(-1-\lambda) = 0.$$

1. Identify the eigenvalues and their multiplicities.
2. For each eigenvalue λ, find a basis of the eigenspace E_λ and state its dimension.
3. Is there a basis of $\mathbb{R}^3$ consisting of eigenvectors of A?

Activity 4.2.5 We will use Sage to find the eigenvalues and eigenvectors of a matrix. Let's begin with the matrix $A = \begin{bmatrix} -3 & 1 \\ 0 & -3 \end{bmatrix}$.

a. We can find the characteristic polynomial of a matrix A by writing `A.charpoly('lambda')`. Notice that we have to give Sage a variable in which to write the polynomial; here, we use `lambda` though `x` works just as well.

```
A = matrix(2,2,[-3,1,0,-3])
A.charpoly('lambda')
```

The factored form of the characteristic polynomial may be more useful since it will tell us the eigenvalues and their multiplicities. The factored characteristic polynomial is found with `A.fcp('lambda')`.

```
A = matrix(2,2,[-3,1,0,-3])
A.fcp('lambda')
```

b. If we only want the eigenvalues, we can use `A.eigenvalues()`.

```
A = matrix(2,2,[-3,1,0,-3])
A.eigenvalues()
```

Notice that the multiplicity of an eigenvalue is the number of times it is repeated in the list of eigenvalues.

c. Finally, we can find eigenvectors by `A.eigenvectors_right()`. (We are looking for *right* eigenvalues since the vector $\mathbf{v}$ appears to the right of A in the definition $A\mathbf{v} = \lambda\mathbf{v}$.)

```
A = matrix(2,2,[-3,1,0,-3])
A.eigenvectors_right()
```

At first glance, the result of this command can be a little confusing to interpret. What we see is a list with one entry for each eigenvalue. For each eigenvalue, there is a triple consisting of (i) the eigenvalue λ, (ii) a basis for E_λ, and (iii) the multiplicity of λ.

d. When working with decimal entries, which are called *floating point numbers* in computer science, we must remember that computers perform only approximate arithmetic. This is a problem when we wish to find the eigenvectors of such a matrix. To illustrate, consider the matrix $A = \begin{bmatrix} 0.4 & 0.3 \\ 0.6 & 0.7 \end{bmatrix}$.

1. Without using Sage, find the eigenvalues of this matrix.
2. What do you find for the reduced row echelon form of $A - I$?
3. Let's now use Sage to determine the reduced row echelon form of $A - I$:

```
A = matrix(2,2,[0.4,0.3,0.6,0.7])
(A-identity_matrix(2)).rref()
```

What result does Sage report for the reduced row echelon form? Why is this result not correct?

4. Because the arithmetic Sage performs with floating point entries is only approximate, we are not able to find the eigenspace E_1. In this next chapter, we will learn how to address this issue. In the meantime, we can get around this problem by writing the entries in the matrix as rational numbers:

```
A = matrix(2,2,[4/10,3/10,6/10,7/10])
A.eigenvectors_right()
```

4.3 Diagonalization, similarity, and powers of a matrix

Preview Activity 4.3.1 In this preview activity, we will review some familiar properties about matrix multiplication that appear in this section.

a. Remember that matrix-vector multiplication constructs linear combinations of the columns of the matrix. For instance, if $A = \begin{bmatrix} \mathbf{a}_1 & \mathbf{a}_2 \end{bmatrix}$, express the product $A\begin{bmatrix} 2 \\ -3 \end{bmatrix}$ in terms of $\mathbf{a}_1$ and $\mathbf{a}_2$.

b. What is the product $A\begin{bmatrix} 4 \\ 0 \end{bmatrix}$ in terms of $\mathbf{a}_1$ and $\mathbf{a}_2$?

c. Next, remember how matrix-matrix multiplication is defined. Suppose that we have matrices A and B and that $B = \begin{bmatrix} \mathbf{b}_1 & \mathbf{b}_2 \end{bmatrix}$. How can we express the matrix product AB in terms of the columns of B?

d. Suppose that A is a matrix having eigenvectors $\mathbf{v}_1$ and $\mathbf{v}_2$ with associated eigenvalues $\lambda_1 = 4$ and $\lambda_2 = -1$. Express the product $A(2\mathbf{v}_1 + 3\mathbf{v}_2)$ in terms of $\mathbf{v}_1$ and $\mathbf{v}_2$.

e. Suppose that A is the matrix from the previous part and that $P = \begin{bmatrix} \mathbf{v}_1 & \mathbf{v}_2 \end{bmatrix}$. What is the matrix product

$$AP = A\begin{bmatrix} \mathbf{v}_1 & \mathbf{v}_2 \end{bmatrix}?$$

Activity 4.3.2 Suppose that A is a 2×2 matrix having eigenvectors $\mathbf{v}_1$ and $\mathbf{v}_2$ with associated eigenvalues $\lambda_1 = 3$ and $\lambda_2 = -6$. Because the eigenvalues are real and distinct, we know by Proposition 4.2.9 that these eigenvectors form a basis of $\mathbb{R}^2$.

a. What are the products $A\mathbf{v}_1$ and $A\mathbf{v}_2$ in terms of $\mathbf{v}_1$ and $\mathbf{v}_2$?

b. If we form the matrix $P = \begin{bmatrix} \mathbf{v}_1 & \mathbf{v}_2 \end{bmatrix}$, what is the product AP in terms of $\mathbf{v}_1$ and $\mathbf{v}_2$?

c. Use the eigenvalues to form the diagonal matrix $D = \begin{bmatrix} 3 & 0 \\ 0 & -6 \end{bmatrix}$ and determine the product PD in terms of $\mathbf{v}_1$ and $\mathbf{v}_2$.

d. The results from the previous two parts of this activity demonstrate that $AP = PD$. Using the fact that the eigenvectors $\mathbf{v}_1$ and $\mathbf{v}_2$ form a basis of $\mathbb{R}^2$, explain why P is invertible and that we must have $A = PDP^{-1}$.

e. Suppose that $A = \begin{bmatrix} -3 & 6 \\ 3 & 0 \end{bmatrix}$. Verify that $\mathbf{v}_1 = \begin{bmatrix} 1 \\ 1 \end{bmatrix}$ and $\mathbf{v}_2 = \begin{bmatrix} 2 \\ -1 \end{bmatrix}$ are eigenvectors of A with eigenvalues $\lambda_1 = 3$ and $\lambda_2 = -6$.

f. Use the Sage cell below to define the matrices P and D and then verify that $A = PDP^{-1}$.

```
# enter the matrices P and D below
P =
D =
P*D*P.inverse()
```

Activity 4.3.3

a. Find a diagonalization of A, if one exists, when

$$A = \begin{bmatrix} 3 & -2 \\ 6 & -5 \end{bmatrix}.$$

b. Can the diagonal matrix

$$A = \begin{bmatrix} 2 & 0 \\ 0 & -5 \end{bmatrix}$$

be diagonalized? If so, explain how to find the matrices P and D.

c. Find a diagonalization of A, if one exists, when

$$A = \begin{bmatrix} -2 & 0 & 0 \\ 1 & -3 & 0 \\ 2 & 0 & -3 \end{bmatrix}.$$

d. Find a diagonalization of A, if one exists, when

$$A = \begin{bmatrix} -2 & 0 & 0 \\ 1 & -3 & 0 \\ 2 & 1 & -3 \end{bmatrix}.$$

e. Suppose that $A = PDP^{-1}$ where

$$D = \begin{bmatrix} 3 & 0 \\ 0 & -1 \end{bmatrix}, \qquad P = \begin{bmatrix} \mathbf{v}_2 & \mathbf{v}_1 \end{bmatrix} = \begin{bmatrix} 2 & 2 \\ 1 & -1 \end{bmatrix}.$$

1. Explain why A is invertible.
2. Find a diagonalization of A^{-1}.
3. Find a diagonalization of A^3.

Activity 4.3.4

a. Let's begin with the diagonal matrix

$$D = \begin{bmatrix} 2 & 0 \\ 0 & -1 \end{bmatrix}.$$

Find the powers D^2, D^3, and D^4. What is D^k for a general value of k?

b. Suppose that A is a matrix with eigenvector $\mathbf{v}$ and associated eigenvalue λ; that is, $A\mathbf{v} = \lambda\mathbf{v}$. By considering $A^2\mathbf{v}$, explain why $\mathbf{v}$ is also an eigenvector of A with eigenvalue λ^2.

c. Suppose that $A = PDP^{-1}$ where

$$D = \begin{bmatrix} 2 & 0 \\ 0 & -1 \end{bmatrix}.$$

Remembering that the columns of P are eigenvectors of A, explain why A^2 is diagonalizable and find a diagonalization in terms of P and D.

d. Give another explanation of the diagonalizability of A^2 by writing

$$A^2 = (PDP^{-1})(PDP^{-1}) = PD(P^{-1}P)DP^{-1}.$$

e. In the same way, find a diagonalization of A^3, A^4, and A^k.

f. Suppose that A is a diagonalizable 2×2 matrix with eigenvalues $\lambda_1 = 0.5$ and $\lambda_2 = 0.1$. What happens to A^k as k becomes very large?

Activity 4.3.5 We begin by rewriting C in terms of r and θ and noting that

$$C = \begin{bmatrix} a & -b \\ b & a \end{bmatrix} = \begin{bmatrix} r\cos\theta & -r\sin\theta \\ r\sin\theta & r\cos\theta \end{bmatrix} = \begin{bmatrix} r & 0 \\ 0 & r \end{bmatrix}\begin{bmatrix} \cos\theta & -\sin\theta \\ \sin\theta & \cos\theta \end{bmatrix}.$$

a. Explain why C has the geometric effect of rotating vectors by θ and scaling them by a factor of r.

b. Let's now consider the matrix

$$A = \begin{bmatrix} -2 & 2 \\ -5 & 4 \end{bmatrix}$$

whose eigenvalues are $\lambda_1 = 1+i$ and $\lambda_2 = 1-i$. We will choose to focus on one of the eigenvalues $\lambda_1 = a+bi = 1+i$.

Form the matrix C using these values of a and b. Then rewrite the point (a,b) in polar coordinates by identifying the values of r and θ. Explain the geometric effect of multiplying vectors by C.

c. Suppose that $P = \begin{bmatrix} 1 & 1 \\ 2 & 1 \end{bmatrix}$. Verify that $A = PCP^{-1}$.

```
C =
P =
P*C*P.inverse()
```

d. Explain why $A^k = PC^kP^{-1}$.

e. We formed the matrix C by choosing the eigenvalue $\lambda_1 = 1+i$. Suppose we had instead chosen $\lambda_2 = 1-i$. Form the matrix C' and use polar coordinates to describe the geometric effect of C.

f. Using the matrix $P' = \begin{bmatrix} 1 & -1 \\ 2 & -1 \end{bmatrix}$, show that $A = P'C'P'^{-1}$.

4.4 Dynamical systems

Preview Activity 4.4.1 Suppose that we have a diagonalizable matrix $A = PDP^{-1}$ where

$$P = \begin{bmatrix} 1 & -1 \\ 1 & 2 \end{bmatrix}, \qquad D = \begin{bmatrix} 2 & 0 \\ 0 & -3 \end{bmatrix}.$$

a. Find the eigenvalues of A and find a basis for the associated eigenspaces.

b. Form a basis of $\mathbb{R}^2$ consisting of eigenvectors of A and write the vector $\mathbf{x} = \begin{bmatrix} 1 \\ 4 \end{bmatrix}$ as a linear combination of basis vectors.

c. Write $A\mathbf{x}$ as a linear combination of basis vectors.

d. For some power k, write $A^k\mathbf{x}$ as a linear combination of basis vectors.

e. Find the vector $A^5\mathbf{x}$.

Activity 4.4.2 Suppose we have two species R and S that interact with each another and that we record the change in their populations from year to year. When we begin our study, the populations, measured in thousands, are R_0 and S_0; after k years, the populations are R_k and S_k.

If we know the populations in one year, suppose that the populations in the following year are determined by the expressions

$$\begin{aligned} R_{k+1} &= 0.9R_k + 0.8S_k \\ S_{k+1} &= 0.2R_k + 0.9S_k. \end{aligned}$$

This is an example of a mutually beneficial relationship between two species. If species S is not present, then $R_{k+1} = 0.9R_k$, which means that the population of species R decreases every year. However, species R benefits from the presence of species S, which helps R to grow by 80% of the population of species S. In the same way, S benefits from the presence of R.

We will record the populations in a vector $\mathbf{x}_k = \begin{bmatrix} R_k \\ S_k \end{bmatrix}$ and note that $\mathbf{x}_{k+1} = A\mathbf{x}_k$ where $A = \begin{bmatrix} 0.9 & 0.8 \\ 0.2 & 0.9 \end{bmatrix}$.

a. Verify that

$$\mathbf{v}_1 = \begin{bmatrix} 2 \\ 1 \end{bmatrix}, \qquad \mathbf{v}_2 = \begin{bmatrix} -2 \\ 1 \end{bmatrix}$$

are eigenvectors of A and find their respective eigenvalues.

b. Suppose that initially $\mathbf{x}_0 = \begin{bmatrix} 2 \\ 3 \end{bmatrix}$. Write $\mathbf{x}_0$ as a linear combination of the eigenvectors $\mathbf{v}_1$ and $\mathbf{v}_2$.

c. Write the vectors $\mathbf{x}_1$, $\mathbf{x}_2$, and $\mathbf{x}_3$ as linear combinations of the eigenvectors $\mathbf{v}_1$ and $\mathbf{v}_2$.

d. What happens to $\mathbf{x}_k$ after a very long time?

e. When k becomes very large, what happens to the ratio of the populations R_k/S_k?

f. After a very long time, by approximately what factor does the population of R grow every year? By approximately what factor does the population of S grow every year?

g. If we begin instead with $\mathbf{x}_0 = \begin{bmatrix} 4 \\ 4 \end{bmatrix}$, what eventually happens to the ratio R_k/S_k as k becomes very large?

Activity 4.4.3 We will now look at several more examples of dynamical systems. If $P = \begin{bmatrix} 1 & -1 \\ 1 & 1 \end{bmatrix}$, we note that the columns of P form a basis $\mathcal{B}$ of $\mathbb{R}^2$. Given below are several matrices A written in the form $A = PEP^{-1}$ for some matrix E. For each matrix, state the eigenvalues of A and sketch a phase portrait for the matrix E on the left and a phase portrait for A on the right. Describe the behavior of $A^k\mathbf{x}_0$ as k becomes very large for a typical initial vector $\mathbf{x}_0$.

a. $A = PEP^{-1}$ where $E = \begin{bmatrix} 1.3 & 0 \\ 0 & 1.5 \end{bmatrix}$.

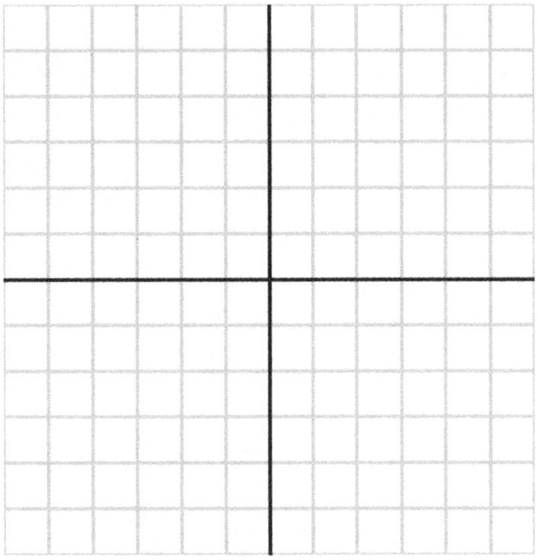

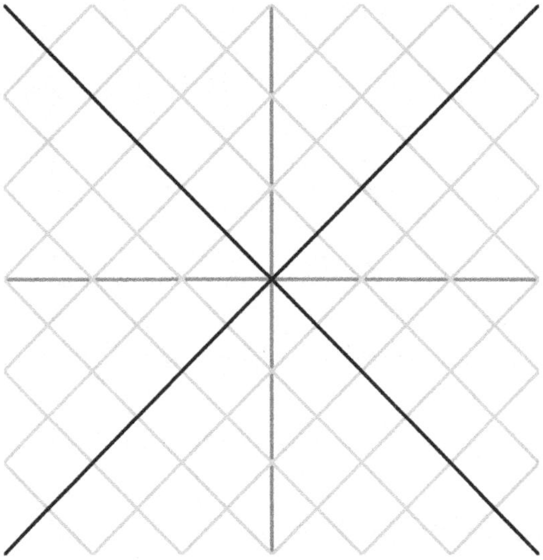

b. $A = PEP^{-1}$ where $E = \begin{bmatrix} 0 & -1 \\ 1 & 0 \end{bmatrix}$.

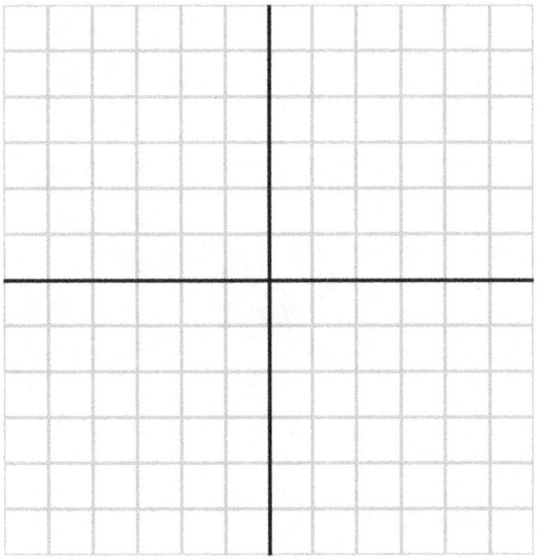

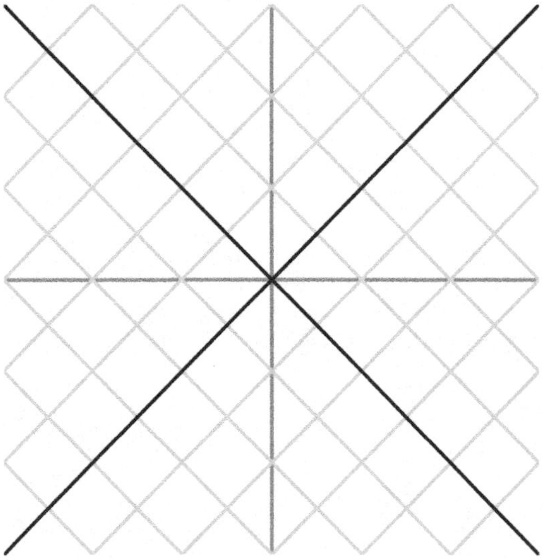

c. $A = PEP^{-1}$ where $E = \begin{bmatrix} 0.7 & 0 \\ 0 & 1.5 \end{bmatrix}$.

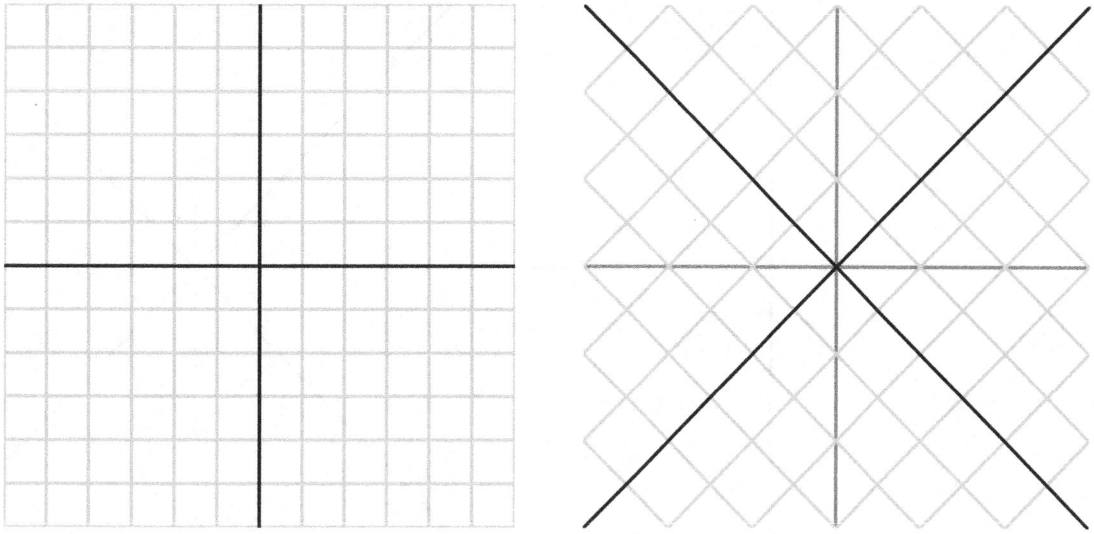

d. $A = PEP^{-1}$ where $E = \begin{bmatrix} 0.3 & 0 \\ 0 & 0.7 \end{bmatrix}$.

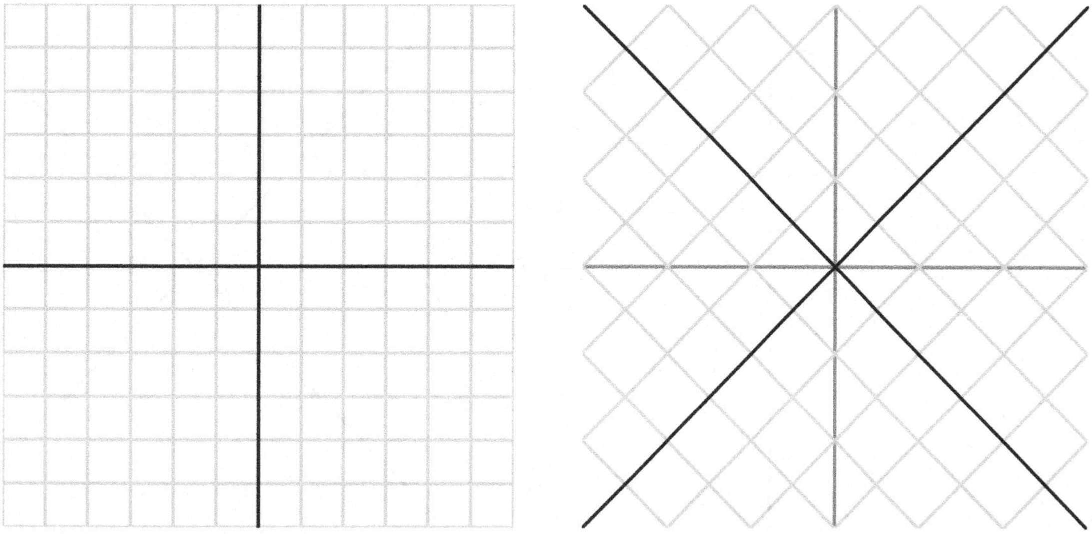

e. $A = PEP^{-1}$ where $E = \begin{bmatrix} 1 & -0.9 \\ 0.9 & 1 \end{bmatrix}$.

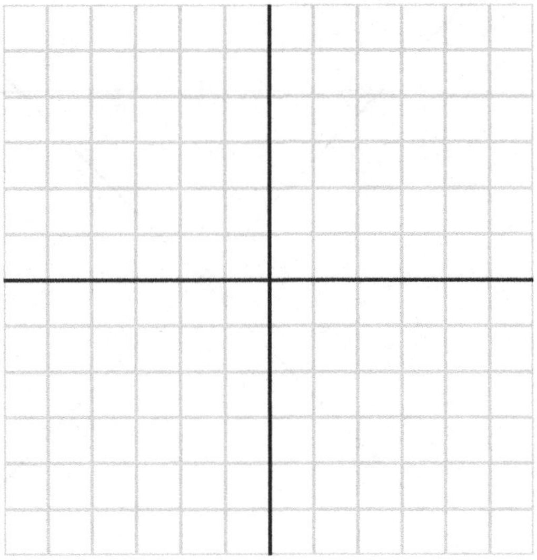

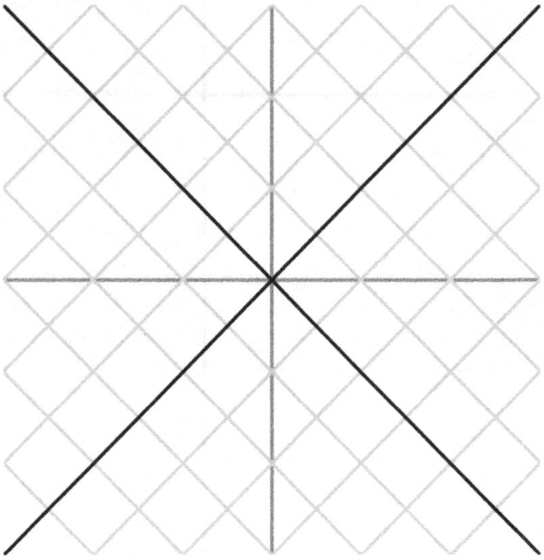

f. $A = PEP^{-1}$ where $E = \begin{bmatrix} 0.6 & -0.2 \\ 0.2 & 0.6 \end{bmatrix}$.

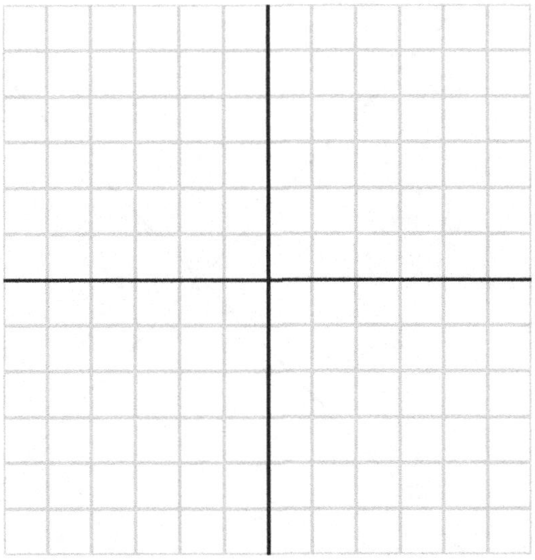

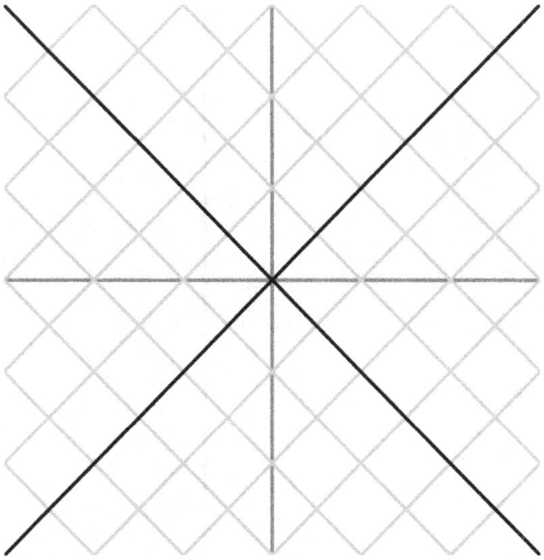

Activity 4.4.4 In this activity, we will consider several ways in which two species might interact with one another. Throughout, we will consider two species R and S whose populations in year k form a vector $\mathbf{x}_k = \begin{bmatrix} R_k \\ S_k \end{bmatrix}$ and which evolve according to the rule

$$\mathbf{x}_{k+1} = A\mathbf{x}_k.$$

a. Suppose that $A = \begin{bmatrix} 0.7 & 0 \\ 0 & 1.6 \end{bmatrix}$.

Explain why the species do not interact with one another. Which of the six types of dynamical systems do we have? What happens to both species after a long time?

b. Suppose now that $A = \begin{bmatrix} 0.7 & 0.3 \\ 0 & 1.6 \end{bmatrix}$.

Explain why S is a beneficial species for R. Which of the six types of dynamical systems do we have? What happens to both species after a long time?

c. If $A = \begin{bmatrix} 0.7 & 0.5 \\ -0.4 & 1.6 \end{bmatrix}$, explain why this describes a predator-prey system. Which of the species is the predator and which is the prey? Which of the six types of dynamical systems do we have? What happens to both species after a long time?

d. Suppose that $A = \begin{bmatrix} 0.5 & 0.2 \\ -0.4 & 1.1 \end{bmatrix}$. Compare this predator-prey system to the one in the previous part. Which of the six types of dynamical systems do we have? What happens to both species after a long time?

Activity 4.4.5 The following type of analysis has been used to study the population of a bison herd. We will divide the population of female bison into three groups: juveniles who are less than one year old; yearlings between one and two years old; and adults who are older than two years.

Each year,

- 80% of the juveniles survive to become yearlings.
- 90% of the yearlings survive to become adults.
- 80% of the adults survive.
- 40% of the adults give birth to a juvenile.

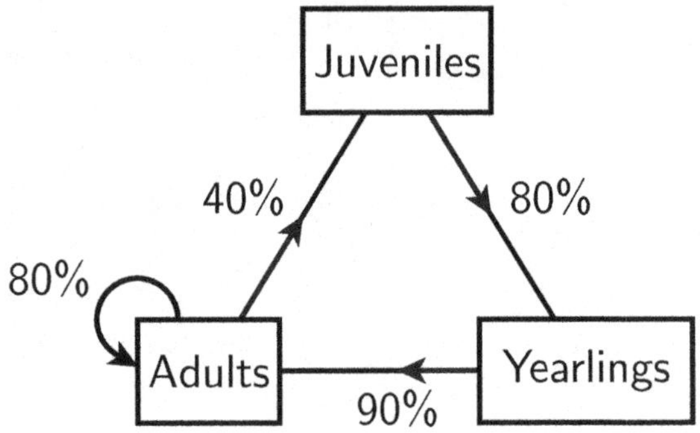

By J_k, Y_k, and A_k, we denote the number of juveniles, yearlings, and adults in year k. We have

$$J_{k+1} = 0.4A_k.$$

a. Find similar expressions for Y_{k+1} and A_{k+1} in terms of J_k, Y_k, and A_k.

b. As is usual, we write the matrix $\mathbf{x}_k = \begin{bmatrix} J_k \\ Y_k \\ A_k \end{bmatrix}$. Write the matrix A such that $\mathbf{x}_{k+1} = A\mathbf{x}_k$ and find its eigenvalues.

c. We can write $A = PEP^{-1}$ where the matrices E and P are approximately:

$$E = \begin{bmatrix} 1.058 & 0 & 0 \\ 0 & -0.128 & -0.506 \\ 0 & 0.506 & -0.128 \end{bmatrix},$$

$$P = \begin{bmatrix} 1 & 1 & 0 \\ 0.756 & -0.378 & 1.486 \\ 2.644 & -0.322 & -1.264 \end{bmatrix}.$$

Make a prediction about the long-term behavior of $\mathbf{x}_k$. For instance, at what rate does it grow? For every 100 adults, how many juveniles, and yearlings are there?

d. Suppose that the birth rate decreases so that only 30% of adults give birth to a juvenile. How does this affect the long-term growth rate of the herd?

e. Suppose that the birth rate decreases further so that only 20% of adults give birth to a juvenile. How does this affect the long-term growth rate of the herd?

f. Find the smallest birth rate that supports a stable population.

4.5 Markov chains and Google's PageRank algorithm

Preview Activity 4.5.1 Suppose that our rental car company rents from two locations P and Q. We find that 80% of the cars rented from location P are returned to P while the other 20% are returned to Q. For cars rented from location Q, 60% are returned to Q and 40% to P.

We will use P_k and Q_k to denote the number of cars at the two locations on day k. The following day, the number of cars at P equals 80% of P_k and 40% of Q_k. This shows that

$$\begin{aligned} P_{k+1} &= 0.8P_k + 0.4Q_k \\ Q_{k+1} &= 0.2P_k + 0.6Q_k. \end{aligned}$$

a. If we use the vector $\mathbf{x}_k = \begin{bmatrix} P_k \\ Q_k \end{bmatrix}$ to represent the distribution of cars on day k, find a matrix A such that $\mathbf{x}_{k+1} = A\mathbf{x}_k$.

b. Find the eigenvalues and associated eigenvectors of A.

c. Suppose that there are initially 1500 cars, all of which are at location P. Write the vector $\mathbf{x}_0$ as a linear combination of eigenvectors of A.

d. Write the vectors $\mathbf{x}_k$ as a linear combination of eigenvectors of A.

e. What happens to the distribution of cars after a long time?

Activity 4.5.2 Suppose you live in a country with three political parties P, Q, and R. We use P_k, Q_k, and R_k to denote the percentage of voters voting for that party in election k.

Voters will change parties from one election to the next as shown in the figure. We see that 60% of voters stay with the same party. However, 40% of those who vote for party P will vote for party Q in the next election.

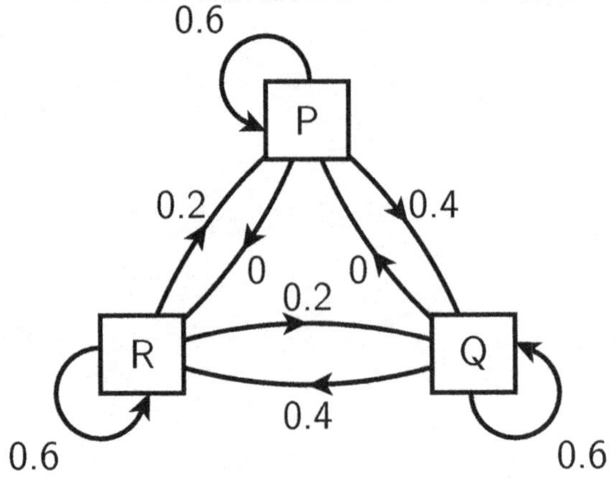

a. Write expressions for P_{k+1}, Q_{k+1}, and R_{k+1} in terms of P_k, Q_k, and R_k.

b. If we write $\mathbf{x}_k = \begin{bmatrix} P_k \\ Q_k \\ R_k \end{bmatrix}$, find the matrix A such that $\mathbf{x}_{k+1} = A\mathbf{x}_k$.

c. Explain why A is a stochastic matrix.

d. Suppose that initially 40% of citizens vote for party P, 30% vote for party Q, and 30% vote for party R. Form the vector $\mathbf{x}_0$ and explain why $\mathbf{x}_0$ is a probability vector.

e. Find $\mathbf{x}_1$, the percentages who vote for the three parties in the next election. Verify that $\mathbf{x}_1$ is also a probability vector and explain why $\mathbf{x}_k$ will be a probability vector for every k.

f. Find the eigenvalues of the matrix A and explain why the eigenspace E_1 is a one-dimensional subspace of $\mathbb{R}^3$.
Then verify that $\mathbf{v} = \begin{bmatrix} 1 \\ 2 \\ 2 \end{bmatrix}$ is a basis vector for E_1.

g. As every vector in E_1 is a scalar multiple of $\mathbf{v}$, find a probability vector in E_1 and explain why it is the only probability vector in E_1.

h. Describe what happens to $\mathbf{x}_k$ after a very long time.

Activity 4.5.3 Consider the matrices

$$A = \begin{bmatrix} 0 & 1 \\ 1 & 0 \end{bmatrix}, \qquad B = \begin{bmatrix} 0.4 & 0.3 \\ 0.6 & 0.7 \end{bmatrix}.$$

a. Verify that both A and B are stochastic matrices.

b. Find the eigenvalues of A and then find a steady-state vector for A.

c. We will form the Markov chain beginning with the vector $\mathbf{x}_0 = \begin{bmatrix} 1 \\ 0 \end{bmatrix}$ and defining $\mathbf{x}_{k+1} = A\mathbf{x}_k$. The Sage cell below constructs the first N terms of the Markov chain with the command `markov_chain(A, x0, N)`. Define the matrix `A` and vector `x0` and evaluate the cell to find the first 10 terms of the Markov chain.

```
def markov_chain(A, x0, N):
    for i in range(N):
        x0 = A*x0
        print (x0)
## define the matrix A and x0
A =
x0 =
markov_chain(A, x0, 10)
```

What do you notice about the Markov chain? Does it converge to the steady-state vector for A?

d. Now find the eigenvalues of B along with a steady-state vector for B.

e. As before, find the first 10 terms in the Markov chain beginning with $\mathbf{x}_0 = \begin{bmatrix} 1 \\ 0 \end{bmatrix}$ and $\mathbf{x}_{k+1} = B\mathbf{x}_k$. What do you notice about the Markov chain? Does it converge to the steady-state vector for B?

f. What condition on the eigenvalues of a stochastic matrix will guarantee that a Markov chain will converge to a steady-state vector?

Activity 4.5.4 We will explore the meaning of the Perron-Frobenius theorem in this activity.

a. Consider the matrix $C = \begin{bmatrix} 0 & 0.5 \\ 1 & 0.5 \end{bmatrix}$. This is a positive matrix, as we saw in the previous example. Find the eigenvectors of C and verify there is a unique steady-state vector.

b. Using the Sage cell below, construct the Markov chain with initial vector $\mathbf{x}_0 = \begin{bmatrix} 1 \\ 0 \end{bmatrix}$ and describe what happens to $\mathbf{x}_k$ as k becomes large.

```
def markov_chain(A, x0, N):
    for i in range(N):
        x0 = A*x0
        print (x0)
## define the matrix C and x0
C =
x0 =
markov_chain(C, x0, 10)
```

c. Construct another Markov chain with initial vector $\mathbf{x}_0 = \begin{bmatrix} 0.2 \\ 0.8 \end{bmatrix}$ and describe what happens to $\mathbf{x}_k$ as k becomes large.

d. Consider the matrix $D = \begin{bmatrix} 0 & 0.5 & 0 \\ 1 & 0.5 & 0 \\ 0 & 0 & 1 \end{bmatrix}$ and compute several powers of D below.

```

```

Determine whether D is a positive matrix.

e. Find the eigenvalues of D and then find the steady-state vectors. Is there a unique steady-state vector?

f. What happens to the Markov chain defined by D with initial vector $\mathbf{x}_0 = \begin{bmatrix} 1 \\ 0 \\ 0 \end{bmatrix}$? What happens to the Markov chain with initial vector $\mathbf{x}_0 = \begin{bmatrix} 0 \\ 0 \\ 1 \end{bmatrix}$.

g. Explain how the matrices C and D, which we have considered in this activity, relate to the Perron-Frobenius theorem.

Activity 4.5.5

We will consider a simple model of the Internet that has three pages and links between them as shown here. For instance, page 1 links to both pages 2 and 3, but page 2 only links to page 1.

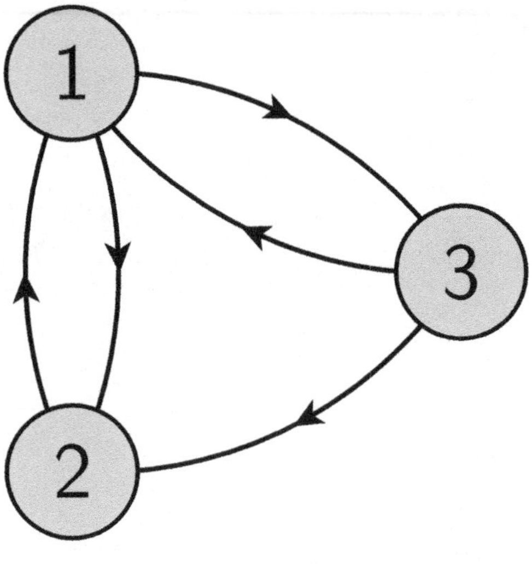

Figure 4.5.7 Our first Internet.

We will measure the quality of the jth page with a number x_j, which is called the PageRank of page j. The PageRank is determined by the following rule: each page divides its PageRank into equal pieces, one for each outgoing link, and gives one piece to each of the pages it links to. A page's PageRank is the sum of all the PageRank it receives from pages linking to it.

For instance, page 3 has two outgoing links. It therefore divides its PageRank x_3 in half and gives half to page 1. Page 2 has only one outgoing link so it gives all of its PageRank x_2 to page 1. We therefore have

$$x_1 = x_2 + \frac{1}{2}x_3.$$

a. Find similar expressions for x_2 and x_3.

b. We now form the PageRank vector $\mathbf{x} = \begin{bmatrix} x_1 \\ x_2 \\ x_3 \end{bmatrix}$. Find a matrix G such that the expressions for x_1, x_2, and x_3 can be written in the form $G\mathbf{x} = \mathbf{x}$. The matrix G is called the "Google matrix".

c. Explain why G is a stochastic matrix.

d. Since $\mathbf{x}$ is defined by the equation $G\mathbf{x} = \mathbf{x}$, any vector in the eigenspace E_1 satisfies this equation. So that we might work with a specific vector, we will define the PageRank vector to be the steady-state vector of the stochastic matrix G. Find this steady-state vector.

e. The PageRank vector $\mathbf{x}$ is composed of the PageRanks for each of the three pages. Which page of the three is assessed to have the highest quality? By referring to the structure of this small model of the Internet, explain why this is a good choice.

f. If we begin with the initial vector $\mathbf{x}_0 = \begin{bmatrix} 1 \\ 0 \\ 0 \end{bmatrix}$ and form the Markov chain $\mathbf{x}_{k+1} = G\mathbf{x}_k$, what does the Perron-Frobenius theorem tell us about the long-term behavior of the Markov chain?

g. Verify that this Markov chain converges to the steady-state PageRank vector.

```
def markov_chain(A, x0, N):
    for i in range(N):
        x0 = A*x0
        print (x0.numerical_approx(digits=3))
## define the matrix G and x0
G =
x0 =
markov_chain(G, x0, 20)
```

Activity 4.5.6 Consider the Internet with eight web pages, shown in Figure 4.5.8.

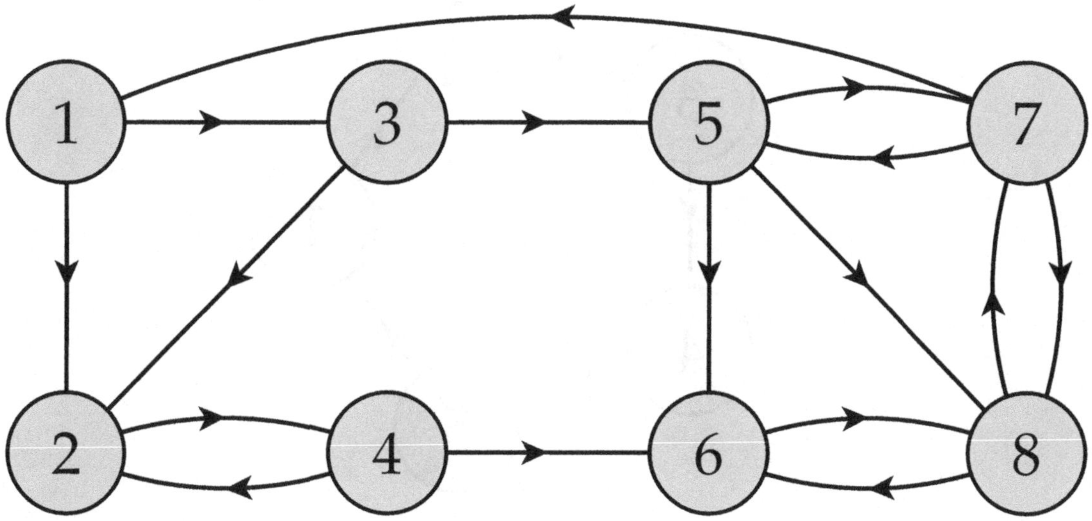

Figure 4.5.8 A simple model of the Internet with eight web pages.

a. Construct the Google matrix G for this Internet. Then use a Markov chain to find the steady-state PageRank vector $\mathbf{x}$.

```
def markov_chain(A, x0, N):
    for i in range(N):
        x0 = A*x0
        print (x0.numerical_approx(digits=3))
## define the matrix G and x0
G =
x0 =
markov_chain(G, x0, 20)
```

b. What does this vector tell us about the relative quality of the pages in this Internet? Which page has the highest quality and which the lowest?

c. Now consider the Internet with five pages, shown in Figure 4.5.9.

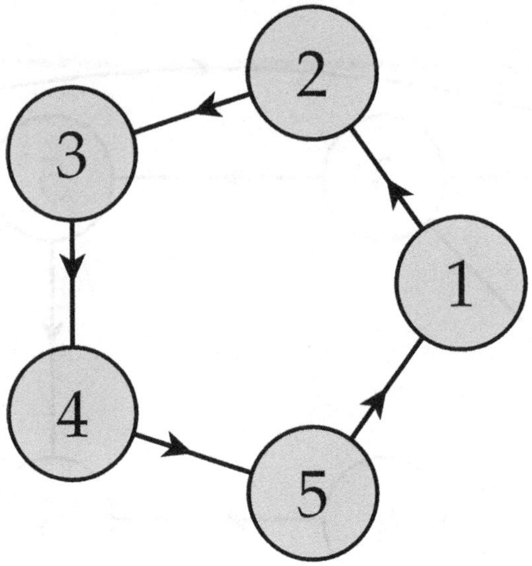

Figure 4.5.9 A model of the Internet with five web pages.

What happens when you begin the Markov chain with the vector $\mathbf{x}_0 = \begin{bmatrix} 1 \\ 0 \\ 0 \\ 0 \\ 0 \end{bmatrix}$? Explain why this behavior is consistent with the Perron-Frobenius theorem.

d. What do you think the PageRank vector for this Internet should be? Is any one page of a higher quality than another?

e. Now consider the Internet with eight web pages, shown in Figure 4.5.10.

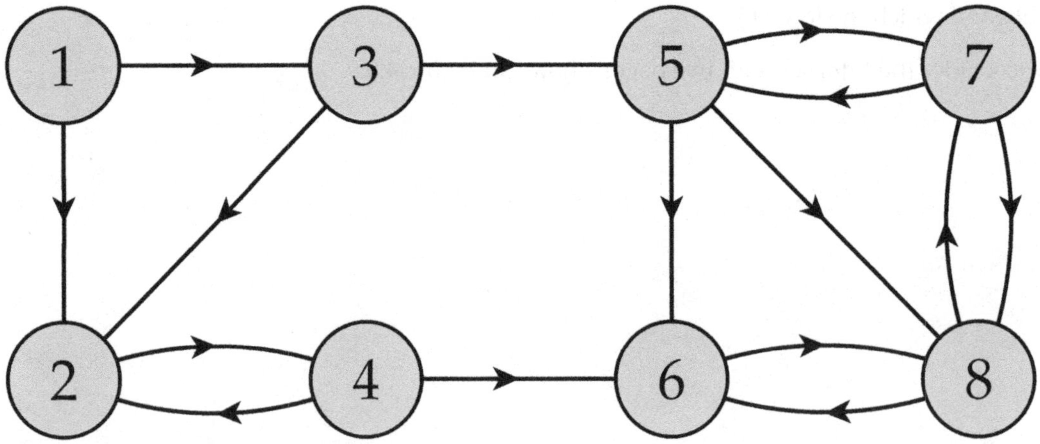

Figure 4.5.10 Another model of the Internet with eight web pages.

Notice that this version of the Internet is identical to the first one that we saw in this activity, except that a single link from page 7 to page 1 has been removed. We can therefore find its Google matrix G by slightly modifying the earlier matrix.

What is the long-term behavior of a Markov chain defined by G and why is this behavior not desirable? How is this behavior consistent with the Perron-Frobenius theorem?

Activity 4.5.7 The following Sage cell will generate the Markov chain for the modified Google matrix G if you simply enter the original Google matrix G in the appropriate line.

```
def modified_markov_chain(A, x0, N):
    r = A.nrows()
    A = 0.85*A + 0.15*matrix(r,r,[1.0/r]*(r*r))
    for i in range(N):
        x0 = A*x0
        print (x0.numerical_approx(digits=3))
## Define original Google matrix G and initial vector x0.
## The function above finds the modified Google matrix
## and resulting Markov chain
G =
x0 =
modified_markov_chain(G, x0, 20)
```

a. Consider the original Internet with three pages shown in Figure 4.5.7 and find the PageRank vector $\mathbf{x}$ using the modified Google matrix in the Sage cell above. How does this modified PageRank vector compare to the vector we found using the original Google matrix G?

b. Find the modified PageRank vector for the Internet shown in Figure 4.5.9. Explain why this vector seems to be the correct one.

c. Find the modified PageRank vector for the Internet shown in Figure 4.5.10. Explain why this modified PageRank vector fixes the problem that appeared with the original PageRank vector.

5 Linear algebra and computing

5.1 Gaussian elimination revisited

Preview Activity 5.1.1 To begin, let's recall how we implemented Gaussian elimination by considering the matrix

$$A = \begin{bmatrix} 1 & 2 & -1 & 2 \\ 1 & 0 & -2 & 1 \\ 3 & 2 & 1 & 0 \end{bmatrix}$$

a. What is the first row operation we perform? If the resulting matrix is A_1, find a matrix E_1 such that $E_1A = A_1$.

b. What is the matrix inverse E_1^{-1}? You can find this using your favorite technique for finding a matrix inverse. However, it may be easier to think about the effect that the row operation has and how it can be undone.

c. Perform the next two steps in the Gaussian elimination algorithm to obtain A_3. Represent these steps using multiplication by matrices E_2 and E_3 so that

$$E_3E_2E_1A = A_3.$$

d. Suppose we need to scale the second row by -2. What is the 3×3 matrix that perfoms this row operation by left multiplication?

e. Suppose that we need to interchange the first and second rows. What is the 3×3 matrix that performs this row operation by left multiplication?

Activity 5.1.2 Suppose we have a hypothetical computer that represents numbers using only three decimal digits. We will consider the linear system

$$\begin{aligned} 0.0001x + y &= 1 \\ x + y &= 2. \end{aligned}$$

a. Show that this system has the unique solution

$$\begin{aligned} x &= \frac{10000}{9999} = 1.00010001\ldots, \\ y &= \frac{9998}{9999} = 0.99989998\ldots. \end{aligned}$$

b. If we represent this solution inside our computer that only holds 3 decimal digits, what do we find for the solution? This is the best that we can hope to find using our computer.

c. Let's imagine that we use our computer to find the solution using Gaussian elimination; that is, after every arithmetic operation, we keep only three decimal digits. Our first step is to multiply the first equation by 10000 and subtract it from the second equation. If we represent numbers using only three decimal digits, what does this give for the value of y?

d. By substituting our value for y into the first equation, what do we find for x?

e. Compare the solution we find on our computer with the actual solution and assess the quality of the approximation.

f. Let's now modify the linear system by simplying interchanging the equations:

$$\begin{aligned} x + y &= 2 \\ 0.0001x + y &= 1. \end{aligned}$$

Of course, this doesn't change the actual solution. Let's imagine we use our computer to find the solution using Gaussian elimination. Perform the first step where we multiply the first equation by 0.0001 and subtract from the second equation. What does this give for y if we represent numbers using only three decimal digits?

g. Substitute the value you found for y into the first equation and solve for x. Then compare the approximate solution found with our hypothetical computer to the exact solution.

h. Which approach produces the most accurate approximation?

Activity 5.1.3 We will consider the matrix

$$A = \begin{bmatrix} 1 & 2 & 1 \\ -2 & -3 & -2 \\ 3 & 7 & 4 \end{bmatrix}$$

and begin performing Gaussian elimination without using partial pivoting.

a. Perform two row replacement operations to find the row equivalent matrix

$$A' = \begin{bmatrix} 1 & 2 & 1 \\ 0 & 1 & 0 \\ 0 & 1 & 1 \end{bmatrix}.$$

Find elementary matrices E_1 and E_2 that perform these two operations so that $E_2E_1A = A'$.

b. Perform a third row replacement to find the upper triangular matrix

$$U = \begin{bmatrix} 1 & 2 & 1 \\ 0 & 1 & 0 \\ 0 & 0 & 1 \end{bmatrix}.$$

Find the elementary matrix E_3 such that $E_3E_2E_1A = U$.

c. We can write $A = E_1^{-1}E_2^{-1}E_3^{-1}U$. Find the inverse matrices E_1^{-1}, E_2^{-1}, and E_3^{-1} and the product $L = E_1^{-1}E_2^{-1}E_3^{-1}$. Then verify that $A = LU$.

d. Suppose that we want to solve the equation $A\mathbf{x} = \mathbf{b} = \begin{bmatrix} 4 \\ -7 \\ 12 \end{bmatrix}$. We will write

$$A\mathbf{x} = LU\mathbf{x} = L(U\mathbf{x}) = \mathbf{b}$$

and introduce an unknown vector $\mathbf{c}$ such that $U\mathbf{x} = \mathbf{c}$. Find $\mathbf{c}$ by noting that $L\mathbf{c} = \mathbf{b}$ and solving this equation.

e. Now that we have found $\mathbf{c}$, find $\mathbf{x}$ by solving $U\mathbf{x} = \mathbf{c}$.

f. Using the factorization $A = LU$ and this two-step process, solve the equation $A\mathbf{x} = \begin{bmatrix} 2 \\ -2 \\ 7 \end{bmatrix}$.

Activity 5.1.4 Sage will create LU factorizations; once we have a matrix `A`, we write `P, L, U = A.LU()` to obtain the matrices P, L, and U such that $PA = LU$.

a. In Example 5.1.1, we found the LU factorization

$$A = \begin{bmatrix} 2 & -3 & 1 \\ -4 & 5 & 0 \\ 2 & -2 & 2 \end{bmatrix} = \begin{bmatrix} 1 & 0 & 0 \\ -2 & 1 & 0 \\ 1 & -1 & 1 \end{bmatrix} \begin{bmatrix} 2 & -3 & 1 \\ 0 & -1 & 2 \\ 0 & 0 & 3 \end{bmatrix} = LU.$$

Using Sage, define the matrix A, and then ask Sage for the LU factorization. What are the matrices P, L, and U?

Notice that Sage finds a different LU factorization than we found in the previous activity because Sage uses partial pivoting, as described in the previous section, when it performs Gaussian elimination.

b. Define the vector $\mathbf{b} = \begin{bmatrix} 8 \\ -13 \\ 8 \end{bmatrix}$ in Sage and compute $P\mathbf{b}$.

c. Use the matrices `L` and `U` to solve $L\mathbf{c} = P\mathbf{b}$ and $U\mathbf{x} = \mathbf{c}$. You should find the same solution $\mathbf{x}$ that you found in the previous activity.

d. Use the factorization to solve the equation $A\mathbf{x} = \begin{bmatrix} 9 \\ -16 \\ 10 \end{bmatrix}$.

e. How does the factorization show us that A is invertible and that, therefore, every equation $A\mathbf{x} = \mathbf{b}$ has a unique solution?

f. Suppose that we have the matrix

$$B = \begin{bmatrix} 3 & -1 & 2 \\ 2 & -1 & 1 \\ 2 & 1 & 3 \end{bmatrix}.$$

Use Sage to find the LU factorization. Explain how the factorization shows that B is not invertible.

g. Consider the matrix

$$C = \begin{bmatrix} -2 & 1 & 2 & -1 \\ 1 & -1 & 0 & 2 \\ 3 & 2 & -1 & 0 \end{bmatrix}$$

and find its LU factorization. Explain why C and U have the same null space and use this observation to find a basis for $\text{Nul}(A)$.

5.2 Finding eigenvectors numerically

Preview Activity 5.2.1 Let's recall some earlier observations about eigenvalues and eigenvectors.

a. How are the eigenvalues and associated eigenvectors of A related to those of A^{-1}?

b. How are the eigenvalues and associated eigenvectors of A related to those of $A - 3I$?

c. If λ is an eigenvalue of A, what can we say about the pivot positions of $A - \lambda I$?

d. Suppose that $A = \begin{bmatrix} 0.8 & 0.4 \\ 0.2 & 0.6 \end{bmatrix}$. Explain how we know that 1 is an eigenvalue of A and then explain why the following Sage computation is incorrect.

```
A = matrix(2,2,[0.8, 0.4, 0.2, 0.6])
I = matrix(2,2,[1, 0, 0, 1])
(A-I).rref()
```

e. Suppose that $\mathbf{x}_0 = \begin{bmatrix} 1 \\ 0 \end{bmatrix}$, and we define a sequence $\mathbf{x}_{k+1} = A\mathbf{x}_k$; in other words, $\mathbf{x}_k = A^k\mathbf{x}_0$. What happens to $\mathbf{x}_k$ as k grows increasingly large?

f. Explain how the eigenvalues of A are responsible for the behavior noted in the previous question.

Activity 5.2.2 Let's begin by considering the matrix $A = \begin{bmatrix} 0.5 & 0.2 \\ 0.4 & 0.7 \end{bmatrix}$ and the initial vector $\mathbf{x}_0 = \begin{bmatrix} 1 \\ 0 \end{bmatrix}$.

a. Compute the vector $\mathbf{x}_1 = A\mathbf{x}_0$.

b. Find m_1, the component of $\mathbf{x}_1$ that has the largest absolute value. Then form $\overline{\mathbf{x}}_1 = \frac{1}{m_1}\mathbf{x}_1$. Notice that the component having the largest absolute value of $\overline{\mathbf{x}}_1$ is 1.

c. Find the vector $\mathbf{x}_2 = A\overline{\mathbf{x}}_1$. Identify the component m_2 of $\mathbf{x}_2$ having the largest absolute value. Then form $\overline{\mathbf{x}}_2 = \frac{1}{m_2}\overline{\mathbf{x}}_1$ to obtain a vector in which the component with the largest absolute value is 1.

d. The Sage cell below defines a function that implements the power method. Define the matrix A and initial vector $\mathbf{x}_0$ below. The command `power(A, x0, N)` will print out the multiplier m and the vectors $\overline{\mathbf{x}}_k$ for N steps of the power method.

```
def power(A, x, N):
    for i in range(N):
        x = A*x
        m = max([comp for comp in x], key=abs).numerical_approx(digits=14)
        x = 1/float(m)*x
        print (m, x)

### Define the matrix A and initial vector x0 below
A =
x0 =
power(A, x0, 20)
```

How does this computation identify an eigenvector of the matrix A?

e. What is the corresponding eigenvalue of this eigenvector?

f. How do the values of the multipliers m_k tell us the eigenvalue associated to the eigenvector we have found?

g. Consider now the matrix $A = \begin{bmatrix} -5.1 & 5.7 \\ -3.8 & 4.4 \end{bmatrix}$. Use the power method to find the dominant eigenvalue of A and an associated eigenvector.

Activity 5.2.3 The key to finding the eigenvalue of A having the smallest absolute value is to note that the eigenvectors of A are the same as those of A^{-1}.

a. If $\mathbf{v}$ is an eigenvector of A with associated eigenvector λ, explain why $\mathbf{v}$ is an eigenvector of A^{-1} with associated eigenvalue λ^{-1}.

b. Explain why the eigenvalue of A having the smallest absolute value is the reciprocal of the dominant eigenvalue of A^{-1}.

c. Explain how to use the power method applied to A^{-1} to find the eigenvalue of A having the smallest absolute value.

d. If we apply the power method to A^{-1}, we begin with an intial vector $\mathbf{x}_0$ and generate the sequence $\mathbf{x}_{k+1} = A^{-1}\mathbf{x}_k$. It is not computationally efficient to compute A^{-1}, however, so instead we solve the equation $A\mathbf{x}_{k+1} = \mathbf{x}_k$. Explain why an LU factorization of A is useful for implementing the power method applied to A^{-1}.

e. The following Sage cell defines a command called `inverse_power` that applies the power method to A^{-1}. That is, `inverse_power(A, x0, N)` prints the vectors $\mathbf{x}_k$, where $\mathbf{x}_{k+1} = A^{-1}\mathbf{x}_k$, and multipliers $\frac{1}{m_k}$, which approximate the eigenvalue of A. Use it to find the eigenvalue of $A = \begin{bmatrix} -5.1 & 5.7 \\ -3.8 & 4.4 \end{bmatrix}$ having the smallest absolute value.

```
def inverse_power(A, x, N):
    for i in range(N):
        x = A \ x
        m = max([comp for comp in x], key=abs).numerical_approx(digits=14)
        x = 1/float(m)*x
        print (1/float(m), x)
### define the matrix A and vector x0
A =
x0 =
inverse_power(A, x0, 20)
```

f. The inverse power method only works if A is invertible. If A is not invertible, what is its eigenvalue having the smallest absolute value?

g. Use the power method and the inverse power method to find the eigenvalues and associated eigenvectors of the matrix $A = \begin{bmatrix} -0.23 & -2.33 \\ -1.16 & 1.08 \end{bmatrix}$.

Activity 5.2.4 Remember that the absolute value of a number tells us how far that number is from 0 on the real number line. We may therefore think of the inverse power method as telling us the eigenvalue closest to 0.

a. If $\mathbf{v}$ is an eigenvector of A with associated eigenvalue λ, explain why $\mathbf{v}$ is an eigenvector of $A - sI$ where s is some scalar.

b. What is the eigenvalue of $A - sI$ associated to the eigenvector $\mathbf{v}$?

c. Explain why the eigenvalue of A closest to s is the eigenvalue of $A - sI$ closest to 0.

d. Explain why applying the inverse power method to $A - sI$ gives the eigenvalue of A closest to s.

e. Consider the matrix $A = \begin{bmatrix} 3.6 & 1.6 & 4.0 & 7.6 \\ 1.6 & 2.2 & 4.4 & 4.1 \\ 3.9 & 4.3 & 9.0 & 0.6 \\ 7.6 & 4.1 & 0.6 & 5.0 \end{bmatrix}$. If we use the power method and inverse power method, we find two eigenvalues, $\lambda_1 = 16.35$ and $\lambda_2 = 0.75$. Viewing these eigenvalues on a number line, we know that the other eigenvalues lie in the range between $-\lambda_1$ and λ_1, as shaded in Figure 5.2.3.

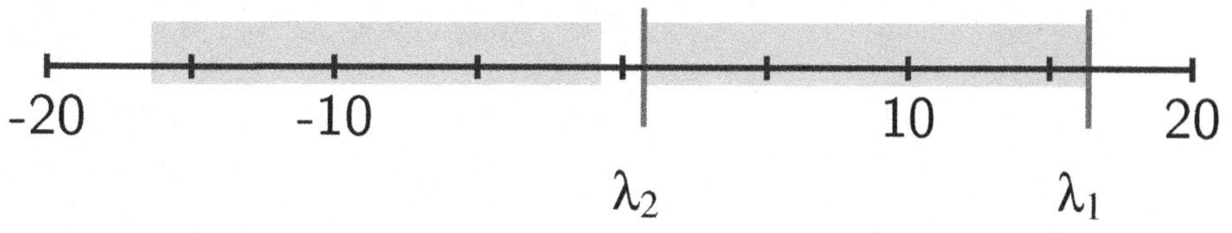

Figure 5.2.3 The range of eigenvalues of A.

The Sage cell below has a function `find_closest_eigenvalue(A, s, x, N)` that implements N steps of the inverse power method using the matrix $A - sI$ and an initial vector x. This function prints approximations to the eigenvalue of A closest to s and its associated eigenvector. By trying different values of s in the shaded regions of the number line shown in Figure 5.2.3, find the other two eigenvalues of A.

```
def find_closest_eigenvalue(A, s, x, N):
    B = A-s*identity_matrix(A.nrows())
    for i in range(N):
        x = B \ x
        m = max([comp for comp in x], key=abs).numerical_approx(digits=14)
        x = 1/float(m)*x
        print (1/float(m)+s, x)
### define the matrix A and vector x0
A =
x0 =
find_closest_eigenvalue(A, 2, x0, 20)
```

f. Write a list of the four eigenvalues of A in increasing order.

6 Orthogonality and Least Squares

6.1 The dot product

Preview Activity 6.1.1

a. Compute the dot product

$$\begin{bmatrix} 3 \\ 4 \end{bmatrix} \cdot \begin{bmatrix} 2 \\ -2 \end{bmatrix}.$$

b. Sketch the vector $\mathbf{v} = \begin{bmatrix} 3 \\ 4 \end{bmatrix}$ below. Then use the Pythagorean theorem to find the length of $\mathbf{v}$.

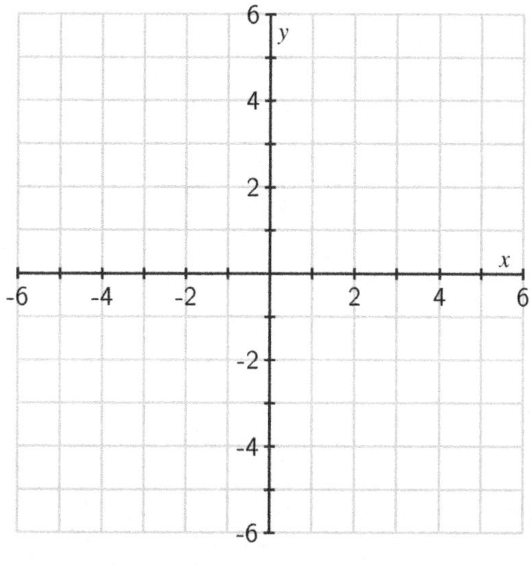

Figure 6.1.1 Sketch the vector $\mathbf{v}$ and find its length.

c. Compute the dot product $\mathbf{v} \cdot \mathbf{v}$. How is the dot product related to the length of $\mathbf{v}$?

d. Remember that the matrix $\begin{bmatrix} 0 & -1 \\ 1 & 0 \end{bmatrix}$ represents the matrix transformation that rotates vectors counterclockwise by 90°. Beginning with the vector $\mathbf{v} = \begin{bmatrix} 3 \\ 4 \end{bmatrix}$, find $\mathbf{w}$, the result of rotating $\mathbf{v}$ by 90°, and sketch it above.

e. What is the dot product $\mathbf{v} \cdot \mathbf{w}$?

f. Suppose that $\mathbf{v} = \begin{bmatrix} a \\ b \end{bmatrix}$. Find the vector $\mathbf{w}$ that results from rotating $\mathbf{v}$ by 90° and find the dot product $\mathbf{v} \cdot \mathbf{w}$.

g. Suppose that $\mathbf{v}$ and $\mathbf{w}$ are two perpendicular vectors. What do you think their dot product $\mathbf{v} \cdot \mathbf{w}$ is?

Activity 6.1.2

a. Sketch the vectors $\mathbf{v} = \begin{bmatrix} 3 \\ 2 \end{bmatrix}$ and $\mathbf{w} = \begin{bmatrix} -1 \\ 3 \end{bmatrix}$ using Figure 6.1.6.

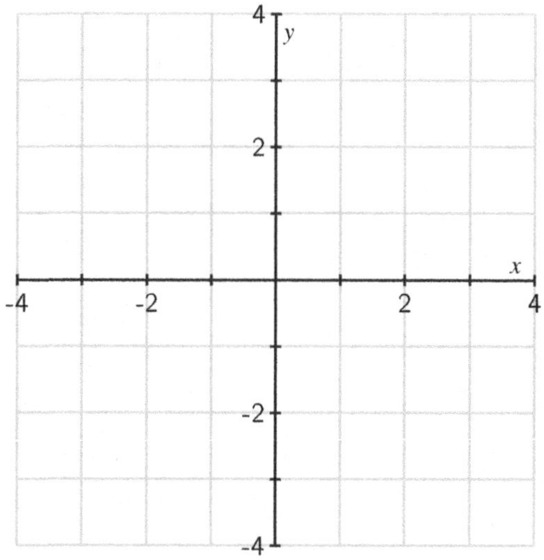

Figure 6.1.6 Sketch the vectors **v** and **w** here.

b. Find the lengths $|\mathbf{v}|$ and $|\mathbf{w}|$ using the dot product.

c. Find the dot product $\mathbf{v} \cdot \mathbf{w}$ and use it to find the angle between **v** and **w**.

d. Consider the vector $\mathbf{x} = \begin{bmatrix} -2 \\ 3 \end{bmatrix}$. Include it in your sketch in Figure 6.1.6 and find the angle between **v** and **x**.

e. If two vectors are perpendicular, what can you say about their dot product? Explain your thinking.

f. For what value of k is the vector $\begin{bmatrix} 6 \\ k \end{bmatrix}$ perpendicular to **w**?

g. Sage can be used to find lengths of vectors and their dot products. For instance, if `v` and `w` are vectors, then `v.norm()` gives the length of `v` and `v * w` gives $\mathbf{v} \cdot \mathbf{w}$.

Suppose that

$$\mathbf{v} = \begin{bmatrix} 2 \\ 0 \\ 3 \\ -2 \end{bmatrix}, \qquad \mathbf{w} = \begin{bmatrix} 1 \\ -3 \\ 4 \\ 1 \end{bmatrix}.$$

Use the Sage cell below to find $|\mathbf{v}|$, $|\mathbf{w}|$, $\mathbf{v} \cdot \mathbf{w}$, and the angle between **v** and **w**. You may use `arccos` to find the angle's measure expressed in radians.

Activity 6.1.2

Activity 6.1.3 This activity explores two further uses of the dot product beginning with the similarity of vectors.

a. Our first task is to assess the similarity between various Wikipedia articles by forming vectors from each of five articles. In particular, one may download the text from a Wikipedia article, remove common words, such as "the" and "and", count the number of times the remaining words appear in the article, and represent these counts in a vector.

For example, evaluate the following cell that loads some special commands along with the vectors constructed from the Wikipedia articles on Veteran's Day, Memorial Day, Labor Day, the Golden Globe Awards, and the Super Bowl. For each of the five articles, you will see a list of the number of times 10 words appear in these articles. For instance, the word "act" appears 3 times in the Veteran's Day article and 0 times in the Labor Day article.

```
url='https://raw.githubusercontent.com/davidaustinm/'
url+='ula_modules/master/dot_similarity.py'
sage.repl.load.load(url, globals())
events.head(int(10))
```

For each of the five articles, we obtain 604-dimensional vectors, which are named `veterans`, `memorial`, `labor`, `golden`, and `super`.

1. Suppose that two articles have no words in common. What is the value of the dot product between their corresponding vectors? What does this say about the angle between these vectors?
2. Suppose there are two articles on the same subject, yet one article is twice as long. What approximate relationship would you expect to hold between the two vectors? What does this say about the angle between them?
3. Use the Sage cell below to find the angle between the vector `veterans` and the other four vectors. To express the angle in degrees, use the `degrees(x)` command, which gives the number of degrees in `x` radians.

```
```

4. Compare the four angles you have found and discuss what they mean about the similarity between the Veteran's Day article and the other four. How do your findings reflect the nature of these five events?

b. Vectors are often used to represent how a quantity changes over time. For instance, the vector $\mathbf{s} = \begin{bmatrix} 78.3 \\ 81.2 \\ 82.1 \\ 79.0 \end{bmatrix}$ might represent the value of a company's stock on four consecutive days. When interpreted in this way, we call the vector a *time series*. Evaluate the Sage cell below to see a representation of two time series $\mathbf{s}_1$, in blue, and $\mathbf{s}_2$, in orange, which we imagine represent the value of two stocks over a period of time. (This cell relies on some data loaded by the first cell in this activity.)

```
series_plot(s1, 'blue') + series_plot(s2, 'orange')
```

Even though one stock has a higher value than the other, the two appear to be related since they seem to rise and fall at roughly similar ways. We often say that they are *correlated*, and we would like to measure the degree to which they are correlated.

1. In order to compare the ways in which they rise and fall, we will first *demean* the time series; that is, for each time series, we will subtract its average value to obtain a new time series. There is a command, `demean(s)`, that returns the demeaned time series of `s`. Use the Sage cell below to demean the series $\mathbf{s}_1$ and $\mathbf{s}_2$ and plot.

```
ds1 = demean(s1)
ds2 = demean(s2)
series_plot(ds1, 'blue') + series_plot(ds2, 'orange')
```

2. If the demeaned series are $\tilde{\mathbf{s}}_1$ and $\tilde{\mathbf{s}}_2$, then the correlation between $\mathbf{s}_1$ and $\mathbf{s}_2$ is defined to be

$$\text{corr}(\mathbf{s}_1, \mathbf{s}_2) = \frac{\tilde{\mathbf{s}}_1 \cdot \tilde{\mathbf{s}}_2}{|\tilde{\mathbf{s}}_1|\,|\tilde{\mathbf{s}}_2|}.$$

   Given the geometric interpretation of the dot product, the correlation equals the cosine of the angle between the demeaned time series, and therefore $\text{corr}(\mathbf{s}_1, \mathbf{s}_2)$ is between -1 and 1.

   Find the correlation between $\mathbf{s}_1$ and $\mathbf{s}_2$.

3. Suppose that two time series are such that their demeaned time series are scalar multiples of one another, as in Figure 6.1.9

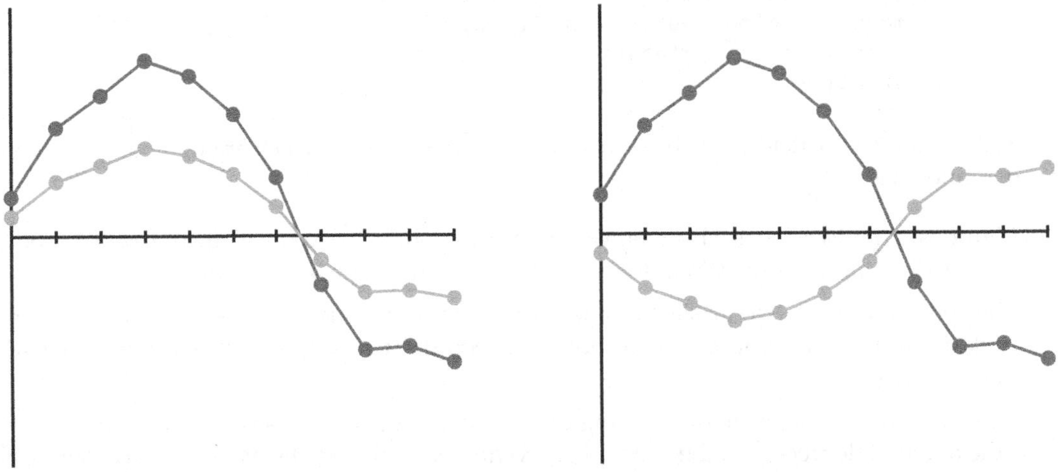

Figure 6.1.9 On the left, the demeaned time series are positive scalar multiples of one another. On the right, they are negative scalar multiples.

   For instance, suppose we have time series $\mathbf{t}_1$ and $\mathbf{t}_2$ whose demeaned time series $\tilde{\mathbf{t}}_1$ and $\tilde{\mathbf{t}}_2$ are positive scalar multiples of one another. What is the angle between the demeaned vectors? What does this say about the correlation $\text{corr}(\mathbf{t}_1, \mathbf{t}_2)$?

4. Suppose the demeaned time series $\tilde{\mathbf{t}}_1$ and $\tilde{\mathbf{t}}_2$ are negative scalar multiples of one another, what is the angle between the demeaned vectors? What does this say about the correlation $\text{corr}(\mathbf{t}_1, \mathbf{t}_2)$?

5. Use the Sage cell below to plot the time series $\mathbf{s}_1$ and $\mathbf{s}_3$ and find their correlation.

```
series_plot(s1, 'blue') + series_plot(s3, 'orange')
```

6. Use the Sage cell below to plot the time series $\mathbf{s}_1$ and $\mathbf{s}_4$ and find their correlation.

```
series_plot(s1, 'blue') + series_plot(s4, 'orange')
```

Activity 6.1.4 To begin, we identify the *centroid*, or the average, of a set of vectors $\mathbf{v}_1, \mathbf{v}_2, \ldots, \mathbf{v}_n$ as

$$\frac{1}{n}(\mathbf{v}_1 + \mathbf{v}_2 + \ldots + \mathbf{v}_n).$$

a. Find the centroid of the vectors

$$\mathbf{v}_1 = \begin{bmatrix} 1 \\ 1 \end{bmatrix}, \mathbf{v}_2 = \begin{bmatrix} 4 \\ 1 \end{bmatrix}, \mathbf{v}_3 = \begin{bmatrix} 4 \\ 4 \end{bmatrix}.$$

and sketch the vectors and the centroid using Figure 6.1.11. You may wish to simply plot the points represented by the tips of the vectors rather than drawing the vectors themselves.

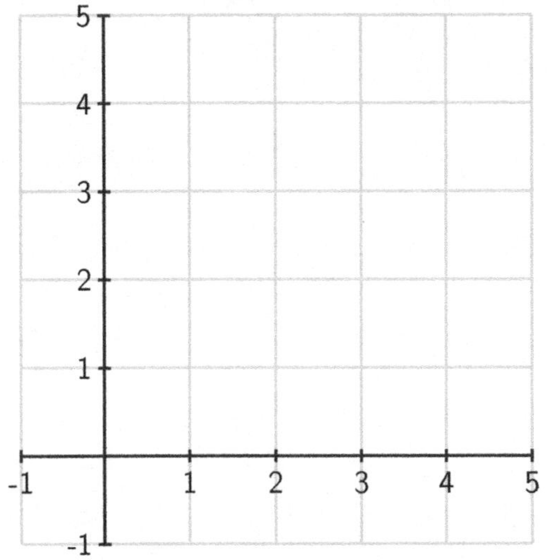

Figure 6.1.11 The vectors $\mathbf{v}_1$, $\mathbf{v}_2$, $\mathbf{v}_3$ and their centroid.

Notice that the centroid lies in the center of the points defined by the vectors.

b. Now we'll illustrate an algorithm that forms clusterings. To begin, consider the following points, represented as vectors,

$$\mathbf{v}_1 = \begin{bmatrix} -2 \\ 1 \end{bmatrix}, \mathbf{v}_2 = \begin{bmatrix} 1 \\ 1 \end{bmatrix}, \mathbf{v}_3 = \begin{bmatrix} 1 \\ 2 \end{bmatrix}, \mathbf{v}_4 = \begin{bmatrix} 3 \\ 2 \end{bmatrix},$$

which are shown in Figure 6.1.12.

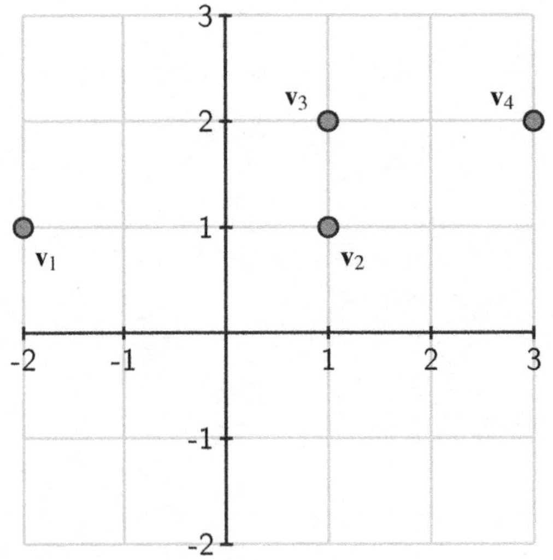

Figure 6.1.12 We will group this set of four points into two clusters.

Suppose that we would like to group these points into $k = 2$ clusters. (Later on, we'll see how to choose an appropriate value for k, the number of clusters.) We begin by choosing two points c_1 and c_2 at random and declaring them to be the "centers"' of the two clusters.

For example, suppose we randomly choose $c_1 = \mathbf{v}_2$ and $c_2 = \mathbf{v}_3$ as the center of two clusters. The cluster centered on $c_1 = \mathbf{v}_2$ will be the set of points that are closer to $c_1 = \mathbf{v}_2$ than to $c_2 = \mathbf{v}_3$. Determine which of the four data points are in this cluster, which we denote by C_1, and circle them in Figure 6.1.12.

c. The second cluster will consist of the data points that are closer to $c_2 = \mathbf{v}_3$ than $c_1 = \mathbf{v}_2$. Determine which of the four points are in this cluster, which we denote by C_2, and circle them in Figure 6.1.12.

d. We now have a clustering with two clusters, but we will try to improve upon it in the following way. First, find the centroids of the two clusters; that is, redefine c_1 to be the centroid of cluster C_1 and c_2 to be the centroid of C_2. Find those centroids and indicate them in Figure 6.1.13

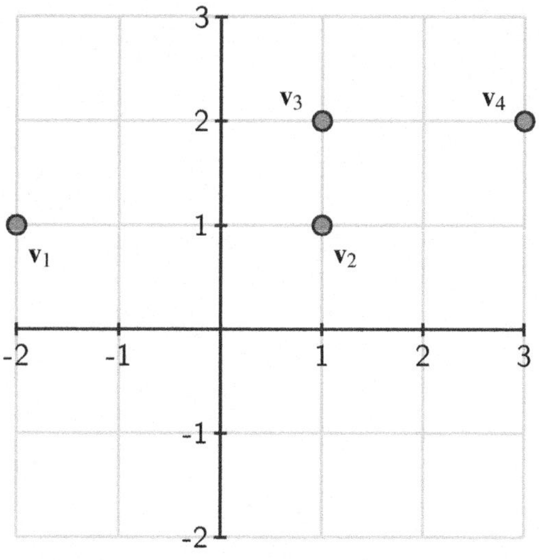

Figure 6.1.13 Indicate the new centroids and clusters.

Now update the cluster C_1 to be the set of points closer to c_1 than c_2. Update the cluster C_2 in a similar way and indicate the clusters in Figure 6.1.13.

e. Let's perform this last step again. That is, update the centroids c_1 and c_2 from the new clusters and then update the clusters C_1 and C_2. Indicate your centroids and clusters in Figure 6.1.14.

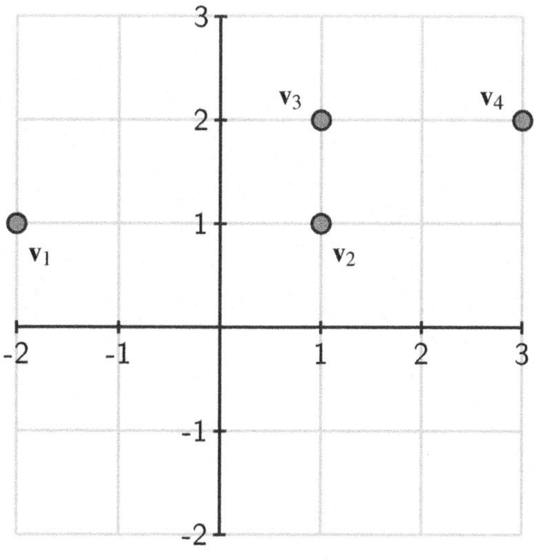

Figure 6.1.14 Indicate the new centroids and clusters.

Notice that this last step produces the same set of clusters so there is no point in repeating it. We declare this to be our final clustering.

Activity 6.1.5 We'll now use the objective to compare clusterings and to choose an appropriate value of k.

a. In the previous activity, one initial choice of c_1 and c_2 led to the clustering:

$$\begin{aligned} C_1 &= \{\mathbf{v}_1\} \\ C_2 &= \{\mathbf{v}_2, \mathbf{v}_3, \mathbf{v}_4\} \end{aligned}$$

with centroids $c_1 = \mathbf{v}_1$ and $c_2 = \begin{bmatrix} 5/3 \\ 5/3 \end{bmatrix}$. Find the objective of this clustering.

b. We have now seen two clusterings and computed their objectives. Recall that our data set is shown in Figure 6.1.12. Which of the two clusterings feels like the better fit? How is this fit reflected in the values of the objectives?

c. Evaluating the following cell will load and display a data set consisting of 177 data points. This data set has the name `data`.

```
url='https://raw.githubusercontent.com/davidaustinm/'
url+='ula_modules/master/k_means.py'
sage.repl.load.load(url, globals())
list_plot(data, color='blue', size=20, aspect_ratio=1)
```

Given this plot of the data, what would seem like a reasonable number of clusters?

d. In the following cell, you may choose a value of k and then run the algorithm to determine and display a clustering and its objective. If you run the algorithm a few times with the same value of k, you will likely see different clusterings having different objectives. This is natural since our algorithm starts by making a random choice of points $c_1, c_2, \ldots, c_k$, and a different choices may lead to different clusterings. Choose a value of k and run the algorithm a few times. Notice that clusterings having lower objectives seem to fit the data better. Repeat this experiment with a few different values of k.

```
k = 2  # you may change the value of k here
clusters, centroids, objective = kmeans(data, k)
print('Objective␣=', objective)
plotclusters(clusters, centroids)
```

e. For a given value of k, our strategy is to run the algorithm several times and choose the clustering with the smallest objective. After choosing a value of k, the following cell will run the algorithm 10 times and display the clustering having the smallest objective.

```
k = 2  # you may change the value of k here
clusters, centroids, objective = minimalobjective(data, k)
print('Objective␣=', objective)
plotclusters(clusters, centroids)
```

For each value of k between 2 and 9, find the clustering having the smallest objective and plot your findings in Figure 6.1.15.

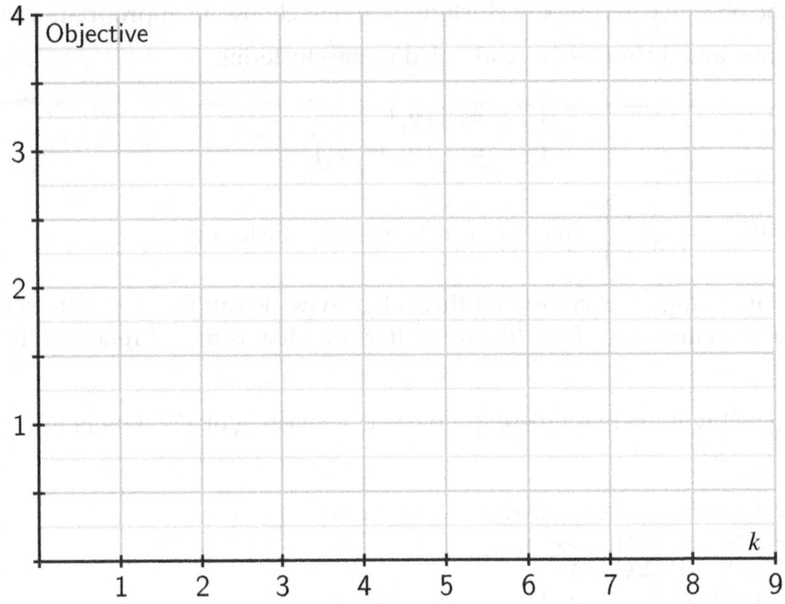

Figure 6.1.15 Construct a plot of the minimal objective as it depends on the choice of k.

This plot is called an *elbow plot* due to its shape. Notice how the objective decreases sharply when k is small and then flattens out. This leads to a location, called the elbow, where the objective transitions from being sharply decreasing to relatively flat. This means that increasing k beyond the elbow does not significantly decrease the objective, which makes the elbow a good choice for k.

Where does the elbow occur in your plot above? How does this compare to the best value of k that you estimated by simply looking at the data in Item c.

Of course, we could increase k until each data point is its own cluster. However, this defeats the point of the technique, which is to group together nearby data points in the hope that they share common features, thus providing insight into the structure of the data.

6.2 Orthogonal complements and the matrix transpose

Preview Activity 6.2.1

a. Sketch the vector $\mathbf{v} = \begin{bmatrix} -1 \\ 2 \end{bmatrix}$ on Figure 6.2.1 and one vector that is orthogonal to it.

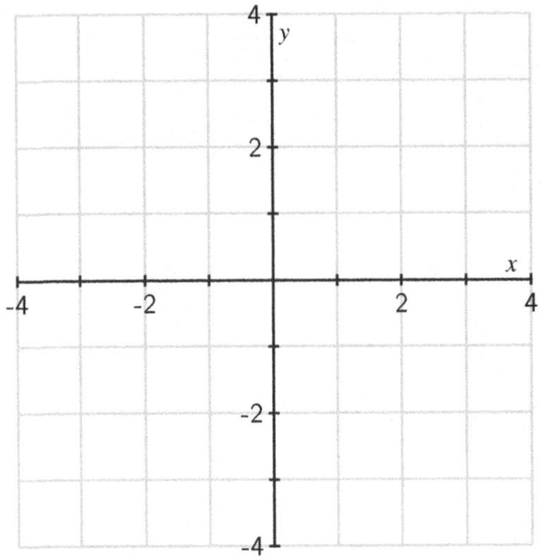

Figure 6.2.1 Sketch the vector **v** and one vector orthogonal to it.

b. If a vector **x** is orthogonal to **v**, what do we know about the dot product $\mathbf{v} \cdot \mathbf{x}$?

c. If we write $\mathbf{x} = \begin{bmatrix} x \\ y \end{bmatrix}$, use the dot product to write an equation for the vectors orthogonal to **v** in terms of x and y.

d. Use this equation to sketch the set of all vectors orthogonal to **v** in Figure 6.2.1.

e. Section 3.5 introduced the column space $\text{Col}(A)$ and null space $\text{Nul}(A)$ of a matrix A. If A is a matrix, what is the meaning of the null space $\text{Nul}(A)$?

f. What is the meaning of the column space $\text{Col}(A)$?

Activity 6.2.2 Suppose that $\mathbf{w}_1 = \begin{bmatrix} 1 \\ 0 \\ -2 \end{bmatrix}$ and $\mathbf{w}_2 = \begin{bmatrix} 1 \\ 1 \\ -1 \end{bmatrix}$ form a basis for W, a two-dimensional subspace of $\mathbb{R}^3$. We will find a description of the orthogonal complement $W^\perp$.

a. Suppose that the vector $\mathbf{x}$ is orthogonal to $\mathbf{w}_1$. If we write $\mathbf{x} = \begin{bmatrix} x_1 \\ x_2 \\ x_3 \end{bmatrix}$, use the fact that $\mathbf{w}_1 \cdot \mathbf{x} = 0$ to write a linear equation for x_1, x_2, and x_3.

b. Suppose that $\mathbf{x}$ is also orthogonal to $\mathbf{w}_2$. In the same way, write a linear equation for x_1, x_2, and x_3 that arises from the fact that $\mathbf{w}_2 \cdot \mathbf{x} = 0$.

c. If $\mathbf{x}$ is orthogonal to both $\mathbf{w}_1$ and $\mathbf{w}_2$, these two equations give us a linear system $B\mathbf{x} = \mathbf{0}$ for some matrix B. Identify the matrix B and write a parametric description of the solution space to the equation $B\mathbf{x} = \mathbf{0}$.

d. Since $\mathbf{w}_1$ and $\mathbf{w}_2$ form a basis for the two-dimensional subspace W, any vector $\mathbf{w}$ in W can be written as a linear combination

$$\mathbf{w} = c_1\mathbf{w}_1 + c_2\mathbf{w}_2.$$

If $\mathbf{x}$ is orthogonal to both $\mathbf{w}_1$ and $\mathbf{w}_2$, use the distributive property of dot products to explain why $\mathbf{x}$ is orthogonal to $\mathbf{w}$.

e. Give a basis for the orthogonal complement $W^\perp$ and state the dimension $\dim W^\perp$.

f. Describe $(W^\perp)^\perp$, the orthogonal complement of $W^\perp$.

Activity 6.2.3 This activity illustrates how multiplying a vector by A^T is related to computing dot products with the columns of A. You'll develop a better understanding of this relationship if you compute the dot products and matrix products in this activity without using technology.

a. If $B = \begin{bmatrix} 3 & 4 \\ -1 & 2 \\ 0 & -2 \end{bmatrix}$, write the matrix B^T.

b. Suppose that

$$\mathbf{v}_1 = \begin{bmatrix} 2 \\ 0 \\ -2 \end{bmatrix}, \qquad \mathbf{v}_2 = \begin{bmatrix} 1 \\ 1 \\ 2 \end{bmatrix}, \qquad \mathbf{w} = \begin{bmatrix} -2 \\ 2 \\ 3 \end{bmatrix}.$$

Find the dot products $\mathbf{v}_1 \cdot \mathbf{w}$ and $\mathbf{v}_2 \cdot \mathbf{w}$.

c. Now write the matrix $A = \begin{bmatrix} \mathbf{v}_1 & \mathbf{v}_2 \end{bmatrix}$ and its transpose A^T. Find the product $A^T\mathbf{w}$ and describe how this product computes both dot products $\mathbf{v}_1 \cdot \mathbf{w}$ and $\mathbf{v}_2 \cdot \mathbf{w}$.

d. Suppose that $\mathbf{x}$ is a vector that is orthogonal to both $\mathbf{v}_1$ and $\mathbf{v}_2$. What does this say about the dot products $\mathbf{v}_1 \cdot \mathbf{x}$ and $\mathbf{v}_2 \cdot \mathbf{x}$? What does this say about the product $A^T\mathbf{x}$?

e. Use the matrix A^T to give a parametric description of all the vectors $\mathbf{x}$ that are orthogonal to $\mathbf{v}_1$ and $\mathbf{v}_2$.

f. Remember that $\text{Nul}(A^T)$, the null space of A^T, is the solution set of the equation $A^T\mathbf{x} = \mathbf{0}$. If $\mathbf{x}$ is a vector in $\text{Nul}(A^T)$, explain why $\mathbf{x}$ must be orthogonal to both $\mathbf{v}_1$ and $\mathbf{v}_2$.

g. Remember that $\text{Col}(A)$, the column space of A, is the set of linear combinations of the columns of A. Therefore, any vector in $\text{Col}(A)$ can be written as $c_1\mathbf{v}_1 + c_2\mathbf{v}_2$. If $\mathbf{x}$ is a vector in $\text{Nul}(A^T)$, explain why $\mathbf{x}$ is orthogonal to every vector in $\text{Col}(A)$.

Activity 6.2.4 In Sage, the transpose of a matrix `A` is given by `A.T`. Define the matrices

$$A = \begin{bmatrix} 1 & 0 & -3 \\ 2 & -2 & 1 \end{bmatrix}, \quad B = \begin{bmatrix} 3 & -4 & 1 \\ 0 & 1 & 2 \end{bmatrix}, \quad C = \begin{bmatrix} 1 & 0 & -3 \\ 2 & -2 & 1 \\ 3 & 2 & 0 \end{bmatrix}.$$

a. Evaluate $(A+B)^T$ and $A^T + B^T$. What do you notice about the relationship between these two matrices?

b. What happens if you transpose a matrix twice; that is, what is $(A^T)^T$?

c. Find $\det(C)$ and $\det(C^T)$. What do you notice about the relationship between these determinants?

d. 1. Find the product AC and its transpose $(AC)^T$.
   2. Is it possible to compute the product $A^T C^T$? Explain why or why not.
   3. Find the product $C^T A^T$ and compare it to $(AC)^T$. What do you notice about the relationship between these two matrices?

e. What is the transpose of the identity matrix I?

f. If a square matrix D is invertible, explain why you can guarantee that D^T is invertible and why $(D^T)^{-1} = (D^{-1})^T$.

Activity 6.2.5

a. Suppose that W is a 5-dimensional subspace of $\mathbb{R}^9$ and that A is a matrix whose columns form a basis for W; that is, $\text{Col}(A) = W$.

1. What is the shape of A?
2. What is the rank of A?
3. What is the shape of A^T?
4. What is the rank of A^T?
5. What is $\dim \text{Nul}(A^T)$?
6. What is $\dim W^\perp$?
7. How are the dimensions of W and $W^\perp$ related?

b. Suppose that W is a subspace of $\mathbb{R}^4$ having basis

$$\mathbf{w}_1 = \begin{bmatrix} 1 \\ 0 \\ 2 \\ -1 \end{bmatrix}, \qquad \mathbf{w}_2 = \begin{bmatrix} -1 \\ 2 \\ -6 \\ 3 \end{bmatrix}.$$

1. Find the dimensions $\dim W$ and $\dim W^\perp$.
2. Find a basis for $W^\perp$. It may be helpful to know that the Sage command `A.right_kernel()` produces a basis for $\text{Nul}(A)$.
3. Verify that each of the basis vectors you found for $W^\perp$ are orthogonal to the basis vectors for W.

6.3 Orthogonal bases and projections

Preview Activity 6.3.1 For this activity, it will be helpful to recall the distributive property of dot products:

$$\mathbf{v}\cdot(c_1\mathbf{w}_1 + c_2\mathbf{w}_2) = c_1\mathbf{v}\cdot\mathbf{w}_1 + c_2\mathbf{v}\cdot\mathbf{w}_2.$$

We'll work with the basis of $\mathbb{R}^2$ formed by the vectors

$$\mathbf{w}_1 = \begin{bmatrix} 1 \\ 2 \end{bmatrix}, \qquad \mathbf{w}_2 = \begin{bmatrix} -2 \\ 1 \end{bmatrix}.$$

a. Verify that the vectors $\mathbf{w}_1$ and $\mathbf{w}_2$ are orthogonal.

b. Suppose that $\mathbf{b} = \begin{bmatrix} 7 \\ 4 \end{bmatrix}$ and find the dot products $\mathbf{w}_1\cdot\mathbf{b}$ and $\mathbf{w}_2\cdot\mathbf{b}$.

c. We would like to express $\mathbf{b}$ as a linear combination of $\mathbf{w}_1$ and $\mathbf{w}_2$, which means that we need to find weights c_1 and c_2 such that

$$\mathbf{b} = c_1\mathbf{w}_1 + c_2\mathbf{w}_2.$$

   To find the weight c_1, dot both sides of this expression with $\mathbf{w}_1$:

$$\mathbf{b}\cdot\mathbf{w}_1 = (c_1\mathbf{w}_1 + c_2\mathbf{w}_2)\cdot\mathbf{w}_1,$$

   and apply the distributive property.

d. In a similar fashion, find the weight c_2.

e. Verify that $\mathbf{b} = c_1\mathbf{w}_1 + c_2\mathbf{w}_2$ using the weights you have found.

Activity 6.3.2 Consider the vectors

$$\mathbf{w}_1 = \begin{bmatrix} 1 \\ -1 \\ 1 \end{bmatrix}, \qquad \mathbf{w}_2 = \begin{bmatrix} 1 \\ 1 \\ 0 \end{bmatrix}, \qquad \mathbf{w}_3 = \begin{bmatrix} 1 \\ -1 \\ -2 \end{bmatrix}.$$

a. Verify that this set forms an orthogonal set of 3-dimensional vectors.

b. Explain why we know that this set of vectors forms a basis for $\mathbb{R}^3$.

c. Suppose that $\mathbf{b} = \begin{bmatrix} 2 \\ 4 \\ -4 \end{bmatrix}$. Find the weights c_1, c_2, and c_3 that express $\mathbf{b}$ as a linear combination $\mathbf{b} = c_1\mathbf{w}_1 + c_2\mathbf{w}_2 + c_3\mathbf{w}_3$ using Proposition 6.3.4.

d. If we multiply a vector $\mathbf{v}$ by a positive scalar s, the length of $\mathbf{v}$ is also multiplied by s; that is, $|s\mathbf{v}| = s\,|\mathbf{v}|$.

Using this observation, find a vector $\mathbf{u}_1$ that is parallel to $\mathbf{w}_1$ and has length 1. Such vectors are called *unit vectors*.

e. Similarly, find a unit vector $\mathbf{u}_2$ that is parallel to $\mathbf{w}_2$ and a unit vector $\mathbf{u}_3$ that is parallel to $\mathbf{w}_3$.

f. Construct the matrix $Q = \begin{bmatrix} \mathbf{u}_1 & \mathbf{u}_2 & \mathbf{u}_3 \end{bmatrix}$ and find the product Q^TQ. Use Proposition 6.2.8 to explain your result.

Activity 6.3.3 This activity demonstrates how to determine the orthogonal projection of a vector onto a subspace of $\mathbb{R}^m$.

a. Let's begin by considering a line L, defined by the vector $\mathbf{w} = \begin{bmatrix} 2 \\ 1 \end{bmatrix}$, and a vector $\mathbf{b} = \begin{bmatrix} 2 \\ 4 \end{bmatrix}$ not on L, as illustrated in Figure 6.3.13.

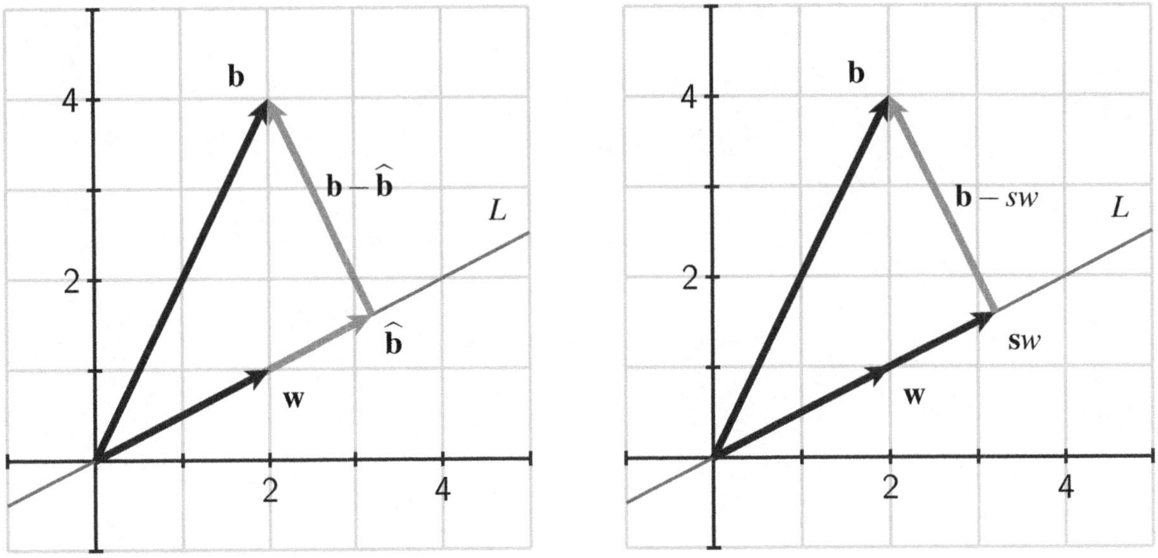

Figure 6.3.13 Finding the orthogonal projection of **b** onto the line defined by **w**.

1. To find $\widehat{\mathbf{b}}$, first notice that $\widehat{\mathbf{b}} = s\mathbf{w}$ for some scalar s. Since $\mathbf{b} - \widehat{\mathbf{b}} = \mathbf{b} - s\mathbf{w}$ is orthogonal to $\mathbf{w}$, what do we know about the dot product
$$(\mathbf{b} - s\mathbf{w}) \cdot \mathbf{w}?$$
2. Apply the distributive property of dot products to find the scalar s. What is the vector $\widehat{\mathbf{b}}$, the orthogonal projection of $\mathbf{b}$ onto L?
3. More generally, explain why the orthogonal projection of $\mathbf{b}$ onto the line defined by $\mathbf{w}$ is
$$\widehat{\mathbf{b}} = \frac{\mathbf{b} \cdot \mathbf{w}}{\mathbf{w} \cdot \mathbf{w}} \mathbf{w}.$$

b. The same ideas apply more generally. Suppose we have an orthogonal set of vectors $\mathbf{w}_1 = \begin{bmatrix} 2 \\ 2 \\ -1 \end{bmatrix}$ and $\mathbf{w}_2 = \begin{bmatrix} 1 \\ 0 \\ 2 \end{bmatrix}$ that define a plane W in $\mathbb{R}^3$. If $\mathbf{b} = \begin{bmatrix} 3 \\ 9 \\ 6 \end{bmatrix}$ another vector in $\mathbb{R}^3$, we seek the vector $\widehat{\mathbf{b}}$ on the plane W closest to $\mathbf{b}$. As before, the vector $\mathbf{b} - \widehat{\mathbf{b}}$ will be orthogonal to W, as illustrated in Figure 6.3.14.

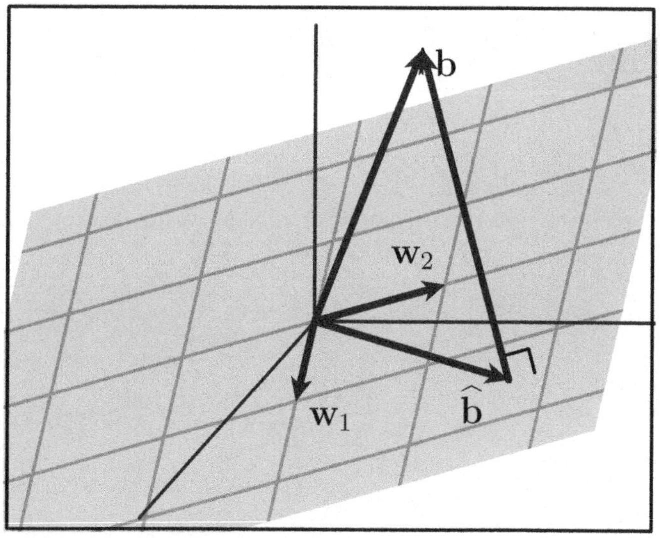

Figure 6.3.14 Given a plane W defined by the orthogonal vectors $\mathbf{w}_1$ and $\mathbf{w}_2$ and another vector $\mathbf{b}$, we seek the vector $\widehat{\mathbf{b}}$ on W closest to $\mathbf{b}$.

1. The vector $\mathbf{b}-\widehat{\mathbf{b}}$ is orthogonal to W. What does this say about the dot products: $(\mathbf{b}-\widehat{\mathbf{b}})\cdot\mathbf{w}_1$ and $(\mathbf{b}-\widehat{\mathbf{b}})\cdot\mathbf{w}_2$?
2. Since $\widehat{\mathbf{b}}$ is in the plane W, we can write it as a linear combination $\widehat{\mathbf{b}} = c_1\mathbf{w}_1 + c_2\mathbf{w}_2$. Then

$$\mathbf{b}-\widehat{\mathbf{b}} = \mathbf{b} - (c_1\mathbf{w}_1 + c_2\mathbf{w}_2).$$

   Find the weight c_1 by dotting $\mathbf{b}-\widehat{\mathbf{b}}$ with $\mathbf{w}_1$ and applying the distributive property of dot products. Similarly, find the weight c_2.
3. What is the vector $\widehat{\mathbf{b}}$, the orthogonal projection of $\mathbf{b}$ onto the plane W?

c. Suppose that W is a subspace of $\mathbb{R}^m$ with orthogonal basis $\mathbf{w}_1, \mathbf{w}_2, \ldots, \mathbf{w}_n$ and that $\mathbf{b}$ is a vector in $\mathbb{R}^m$. Explain why the orthogonal projection of $\mathbf{b}$ onto W is the vector

$$\widehat{\mathbf{b}} = \frac{\mathbf{b}\cdot\mathbf{w}_1}{\mathbf{w}_1\cdot\mathbf{w}_1}\mathbf{w}_1 + \frac{\mathbf{b}\cdot\mathbf{w}_2}{\mathbf{w}_2\cdot\mathbf{w}_2}\mathbf{w}_2 + \cdots + \frac{\mathbf{b}\cdot\mathbf{w}_n}{\mathbf{w}_n\cdot\mathbf{w}_n}\mathbf{w}_n.$$

d. Suppose that $\mathbf{u}_1, \mathbf{u}_2, \ldots, \mathbf{u}_n$ is an *orthonormal* basis for W; that is, the vectors are orthogonal to one another and have unit length. Explain why the orthogonal projection is

$$\widehat{\mathbf{b}} = (\mathbf{b}\cdot\mathbf{u}_1)\,\mathbf{u}_1 + (\mathbf{b}\cdot\mathbf{u}_2)\,\mathbf{u}_2 + \cdots + (\mathbf{b}\cdot\mathbf{u}_n)\,\mathbf{u}_n.$$

e. If $Q = \begin{bmatrix}\mathbf{u}_1 & \mathbf{u}_2 & \ldots & \mathbf{u}_n\end{bmatrix}$ is the matrix whose columns are an orthonormal basis of W, use Proposition 6.2.8 to explain why $\widehat{\mathbf{b}} = QQ^T\mathbf{b}$.

Activity 6.3.4

a. Suppose that L is the line in $\mathbb{R}^3$ defined by the vector $\mathbf{w} = \begin{bmatrix} 1 \\ 2 \\ -2 \end{bmatrix}$.

1. Find an orthonormal basis $\mathbf{u}$ for L.
2. Construct the matrix $Q = \begin{bmatrix} \mathbf{u} \end{bmatrix}$ and use it to construct the matrix P that projects vectors orthogonally onto L.
3. Use your matrix to find $\widehat{\mathbf{b}}$, the orthogonal projection of $\mathbf{b} = \begin{bmatrix} 1 \\ 1 \\ 1 \end{bmatrix}$ onto L.
4. Find $\text{rank}(P)$ and explain its geometric significance.

b. The vectors

$$\mathbf{w}_1 = \begin{bmatrix} 1 \\ 1 \\ 1 \\ 1 \end{bmatrix}, \qquad \mathbf{w}_2 = \begin{bmatrix} 0 \\ 1 \\ 1 \\ -2 \end{bmatrix}$$

form an orthogonal basis of W, a two-dimensional subspace of $\mathbb{R}^4$.

1. Use the projection formula from Proposition 6.3.15 to find $\widehat{\mathbf{b}}$, the orthogonal projection of $\mathbf{b} = \begin{bmatrix} 9 \\ 2 \\ -2 \\ 3 \end{bmatrix}$ onto W.
2. Find an orthonormal basis $\mathbf{u}_1$ and $\mathbf{u}_2$ for W and use it to construct the matrix P that projects vectors orthogonally onto W. Check that $P\mathbf{b} = \widehat{\mathbf{b}}$, the orthogonal projection you found in the previous part of this activity.
3. Find $\text{rank}(P)$ and explain its geometric significance.
4. Find a basis for $W^\perp$.
5. Find a vector $\mathbf{b}^\perp$ in $W^\perp$ such that
$$\mathbf{b} = \widehat{\mathbf{b}} + \mathbf{b}^\perp.$$
6. If Q is the matrix whose columns are $\mathbf{u}_1$ and $\mathbf{u}_2$, find the product Q^TQ and explain your result.

6.4 Finding orthogonal bases

Preview Activity 6.4.1 Suppose we have a basis for $\mathbb{R}^2$ consisting of the vectors

$$\mathbf{v}_1 = \begin{bmatrix} 1 \\ 1 \end{bmatrix}, \qquad \mathbf{v}_2 = \begin{bmatrix} 0 \\ 2 \end{bmatrix}$$

as shown in Figure 6.4.1. Notice that this basis is not orthogonal.

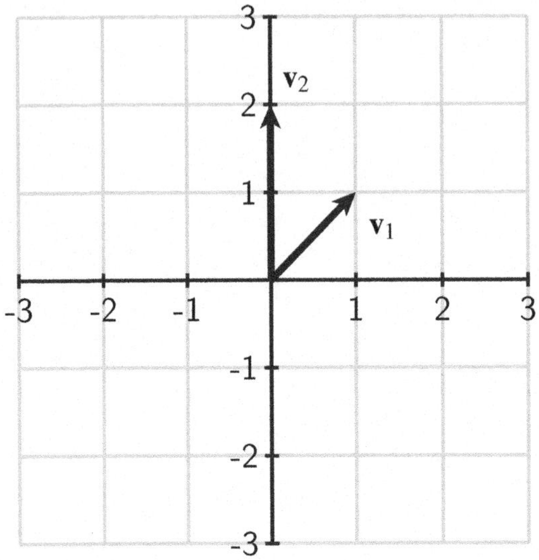

Figure 6.4.1 A basis for $\mathbb{R}^2$.

a. Find the vector $\widehat{\mathbf{v}}_2$ that is the orthogonal projection of $\mathbf{v}_2$ onto the line defined by $\mathbf{v}_1$.

b. Explain why $\mathbf{v}_2 - \widehat{\mathbf{v}}_2$ is orthogonal to $\mathbf{v}_1$.

c. Define the new vectors $\mathbf{w}_1 = \mathbf{v}_1$ and $\mathbf{w}_2 = \mathbf{v}_2 - \widehat{\mathbf{v}}_2$ and sketch them in Figure 6.4.2. Explain why $\mathbf{w}_1$ and $\mathbf{w}_2$ define an orthogonal basis for $\mathbb{R}^2$.

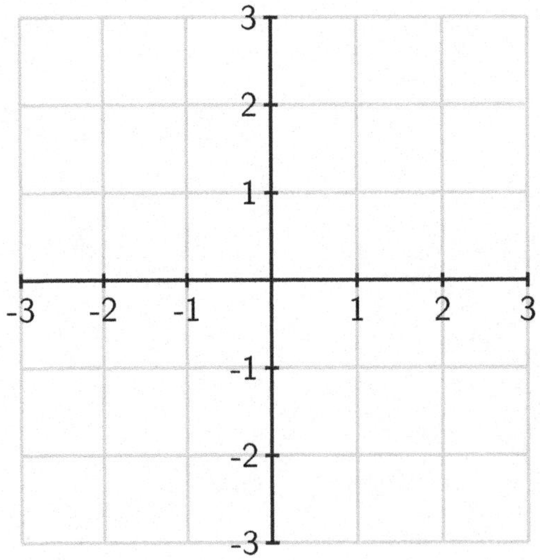

Figure 6.4.2 Sketch the new basis $\mathbf{w}_1$ and $\mathbf{w}_2$.

d. Write the vector $\mathbf{b} = \begin{bmatrix} 8 \\ -10 \end{bmatrix}$ as a linear combination of $\mathbf{w}_1$ and $\mathbf{w}_2$.

e. Scale the vectors $\mathbf{w}_1$ and $\mathbf{w}_2$ to produce an orthonormal basis $\mathbf{u}_1$ and $\mathbf{u}_2$ for $\mathbb{R}^2$.

Activity 6.4.2 Suppose that W is a three-dimensional subspace of $\mathbb{R}^4$ with basis:

$$\mathbf{v}_1 = \begin{bmatrix} 1 \\ 1 \\ 1 \\ 1 \end{bmatrix}, \quad \mathbf{v}_2 = \begin{bmatrix} 1 \\ 3 \\ 2 \\ 2 \end{bmatrix}, \quad \mathbf{v}_3 = \begin{bmatrix} 1 \\ -3 \\ -3 \\ -3 \end{bmatrix}.$$

We can see that this basis is not orthogonal by noting that $\mathbf{v}_1 \cdot \mathbf{v}_2 = 8$. Our goal is to create an orthogonal basis $\mathbf{w}_1$, $\mathbf{w}_2$, and $\mathbf{w}_3$ for W.

To begin, we declare that $\mathbf{w}_1 = \mathbf{v}_1$, and we call W_1 the line defined by $\mathbf{w}_1$.

a. Find the vector $\widehat{\mathbf{v}}_2$ that is the orthogonal projection of $\mathbf{v}_2$ onto W_1, the line defined by $\mathbf{w}_1$.

b. Form the vector $\mathbf{w}_2 = \mathbf{v}_2 - \widehat{\mathbf{v}}_2$ and verify that it is orthogonal to $\mathbf{w}_1$.

c. Explain why $\text{Span}\{\mathbf{w}_1, \mathbf{w}_2\} = \text{Span}\{\mathbf{v}_1, \mathbf{v}_2\}$ by showing that any linear combination of $\mathbf{v}_1$ and $\mathbf{v}_2$ can be written as a linear combination of $\mathbf{w}_1$ and $\mathbf{w}_2$ and vice versa.

d. The vectors $\mathbf{w}_1$ and $\mathbf{w}_2$ are an orthogonal basis for a two-dimensional subspace W_2 of $\mathbb{R}^4$. Find the vector $\widehat{\mathbf{v}}_3$ that is the orthogonal projection of $\mathbf{v}_3$ onto W_2.

e. Verify that $\mathbf{w}_3 = \mathbf{v}_3 - \widehat{\mathbf{v}}_3$ is orthogonal to both $\mathbf{w}_1$ and $\mathbf{w}_2$.

f. Explain why $\mathbf{w}_1$, $\mathbf{w}_2$, and $\mathbf{w}_3$ form an orthogonal basis for W.

g. Now find an orthonormal basis for W.

Activity 6.4.3 Sage can automate these computations for us. Before we begin, however, it will be helpful to understand how we can combine things using a `list` in Python. For instance, if the vectors `v1`, `v2`, and `v3` form a basis for a subspace, we can bundle them together using square brackets: `[v1, v2, v3]`. Furthermore, we could assign this to a variable, such as `basis = [v1, v2, v3]`.

Evaluating the following cell will load in some special commands.

```
url='https://raw.githubusercontent.com/davidaustinm/'
url+='ula_modules/master/orthogonality.py'
sage.repl.load.load(url, globals())
```

- There is a command to apply the projection formula: `projection(b, basis)` returns the orthogonal projection of `b` onto the subspace spanned by `basis`, which is a list of vectors.
- The command `unit(w)` returns a unit vector parallel to `w`.
- Given a collection of vectors, say, `v1` and `v2`, we can form the matrix whose columns are `v1` and `v2` using `matrix([v1, v2]).T`. When given a `list` of vectors, Sage constructs a matrix whose *rows* are the given vectors. For this reason, we need to apply the transpose.

Let's now consider W, the subspace of $\mathbb{R}^5$ having basis

$$\mathbf{v}_1 = \begin{bmatrix} 14 \\ -6 \\ 8 \\ 2 \\ -6 \end{bmatrix}, \quad \mathbf{v}_2 = \begin{bmatrix} 5 \\ -3 \\ 4 \\ 3 \\ -7 \end{bmatrix}, \quad \mathbf{v}_3 = \begin{bmatrix} 2 \\ 3 \\ 0 \\ -2 \\ 1 \end{bmatrix}.$$

a. Apply the Gram-Schmidt algorithm to find an orthogonal basis $\mathbf{w}_1$, $\mathbf{w}_2$, and $\mathbf{w}_3$ for W.

b. Find $\widehat{\mathbf{b}}$, the orthogonal projection of $\mathbf{b} = \begin{bmatrix} -5 \\ 11 \\ 0 \\ -1 \\ 5 \end{bmatrix}$ onto W.

c. Explain why we know that $\widehat{\mathbf{b}}$ is a linear combination of the original vectors $\mathbf{v}_1$, $\mathbf{v}_2$, and $\mathbf{v}_3$ and then find weights so that

$$\widehat{\mathbf{b}} = c_1\mathbf{v}_1 + c_2\mathbf{v}_2 + c_3\mathbf{v}_3.$$

d. Find an orthonormal basis $\mathbf{u}_1$, $\mathbf{u}_2$, for $\mathbf{u}_3$ for W and form the matrix Q whose columns are these vectors.

e. Find the product Q^TQ and explain the result.

f. Find the matrix P that projects vectors orthogonally onto W and verify that $P\mathbf{b}$ gives $\widehat{\mathbf{b}}$, the orthogonal projection that you found earlier.

Activity 6.4.4 Suppose that A is the 4×3 matrix whose columns are

$$\mathbf{v}_1 = \begin{bmatrix} 1 \\ 1 \\ 1 \\ 1 \end{bmatrix}, \quad \mathbf{v}_2 = \begin{bmatrix} 1 \\ 3 \\ 2 \\ 2 \end{bmatrix}, \quad \mathbf{v}_3 = \begin{bmatrix} 1 \\ -3 \\ -3 \\ -3 \end{bmatrix}.$$

These vectors form a basis for W, the subspace of $\mathbb{R}^4$ that we encountered in Activity 6.4.2. Since these vectors are the columns of A, we have $\text{Col}(A) = W$.

a. When we implemented Gram-Schmidt, we first found an orthogonal basis $\mathbf{w}_1$, $\mathbf{w}_2$, and $\mathbf{w}_3$ using

$$\begin{aligned} \mathbf{w}_1 &= \mathbf{v}_1 \\ \mathbf{w}_2 &= \mathbf{v}_2 - \frac{\mathbf{v}_2 \cdot \mathbf{w}_1}{\mathbf{w}_1 \cdot \mathbf{w}_1}\mathbf{w}_1 \\ \mathbf{w}_3 &= \mathbf{v}_3 - \frac{\mathbf{v}_3 \cdot \mathbf{w}_1}{\mathbf{w}_1 \cdot \mathbf{w}_1}\mathbf{w}_1 - \frac{\mathbf{v}_3 \cdot \mathbf{w}_2}{\mathbf{w}_2 \cdot \mathbf{w}_2}\mathbf{w}_2. \end{aligned}$$

Use these expressions to write $\mathbf{v}_1$, $\mathbf{v}_1$, and $\mathbf{v}_3$ as linear combinations of $\mathbf{w}_1$, $\mathbf{w}_2$, and $\mathbf{w}_3$.

b. We next normalized the orthogonal basis $\mathbf{w}_1$, $\mathbf{w}_2$, and $\mathbf{w}_3$ to obtain an orthonormal basis $\mathbf{u}_1$, $\mathbf{u}_2$, and $\mathbf{u}_3$.

Write the vectors $\mathbf{w}_i$ as scalar multiples of $\mathbf{u}_i$. Then use these expressions to write $\mathbf{v}_1$, $\mathbf{v}_1$, and $\mathbf{v}_3$ as linear combinations of $\mathbf{u}_1$, $\mathbf{u}_2$, and $\mathbf{u}_3$.

c. Suppose that $Q = \begin{bmatrix} \mathbf{u}_1 & \mathbf{u}_2 & \mathbf{u}_3 \end{bmatrix}$. Use the result of the previous part to find a vector $\mathbf{r}_1$ so that $Q\mathbf{r}_1 = \mathbf{v}_1$.

d. Then find vectors $\mathbf{r}_2$ and $\mathbf{r}_3$ such that $Q\mathbf{r}_2 = \mathbf{v}_2$ and $Q\mathbf{r}_3 = \mathbf{v}_3$.

e. Construct the matrix $R = \begin{bmatrix} \mathbf{r}_1 & \mathbf{r}_2 & \mathbf{r}_3 \end{bmatrix}$. Remembering that $A = \begin{bmatrix} \mathbf{v}_1 & \mathbf{v}_2 & \mathbf{v}_3 \end{bmatrix}$, explain why $A = QR$.

f. What is special about the shape of R?

g. Suppose that A is a 10×6 matrix whose columns are linearly independent. This means that the columns of A form a basis for $W = \text{Col}(A)$, a 6-dimensional subspace of $\mathbb{R}^{10}$. Suppose that we apply Gram-Schmidt orthogonalization to create an orthonormal basis whose vectors form the columns of Q and that we write $A = QR$. What are the shape of Q and what the shape of R?

Activity 6.4.5 As before, we would like to use Sage to automate the process of finding and using the QR factorization of a matrix A. Evaluating the following cell provides a command `QR(A)` that returns the factorization, which may be stored using, for example, `Q, R = QR(A)`.

```
url='https://raw.githubusercontent.com/davidaustinm/'
url+='ula_modules/master/orthogonality.py'
sage.repl.load.load(url, globals())
```

Suppose that A is the following matrix whose columns are linearly independent.

$$A = \begin{bmatrix} 1 & 0 & -3 \\ 0 & 2 & -1 \\ 1 & 0 & 1 \\ 1 & 3 & 5 \end{bmatrix}.$$

a. If $A = QR$, what is the shape of Q and R? What is special about the form of R?

b. Find the QR factorization using `Q, R = QR(A)` and verify that R has the predicted shape and that $A = QR$.

```

```

c. Find the matrix P that orthogonally projects vectors onto $\text{Col}(A)$.

d. Find $\widehat{\mathbf{b}}$, the orthogonal projection of $\mathbf{b} = \begin{bmatrix} 4 \\ -17 \\ -14 \\ 22 \end{bmatrix}$ onto $\text{Col}(A)$.

e. Explain why the equation $A\mathbf{x} = \widehat{\mathbf{b}}$ must be consistent and then find $\mathbf{x}$.

6.5 Orthogonal least squares

Preview Activity 6.5.1

a. Is there a solution to the equation $A\mathbf{x} = \mathbf{b}$ where A and $\mathbf{b}$ are such that

$$\begin{bmatrix} 1 & 2 \\ 2 & 5 \\ -1 & 0 \end{bmatrix} \mathbf{x} = \begin{bmatrix} 5 \\ -3 \\ -1 \end{bmatrix}.$$

b. We know that $\begin{bmatrix} 1 \\ 2 \\ -1 \end{bmatrix}$ and $\begin{bmatrix} 2 \\ 5 \\ 0 \end{bmatrix}$ form a basis for Col(A). Find an orthogonal basis for Col(A).

c. Find the orthogonal projection $\widehat{\mathbf{b}}$ of $\mathbf{b}$ onto Col(A).

d. Explain why the equation $A\mathbf{x} = \widehat{\mathbf{b}}$ must be consistent and then find its solution.

Activity 6.5.2 Suppose we have three data points $(1,1)$, $(2,1)$, and $(3,3)$ and that we would like to find a line passing through them.

a. Plot these three points in Figure 6.5.2. Are you able to draw a line that passes through all three points?

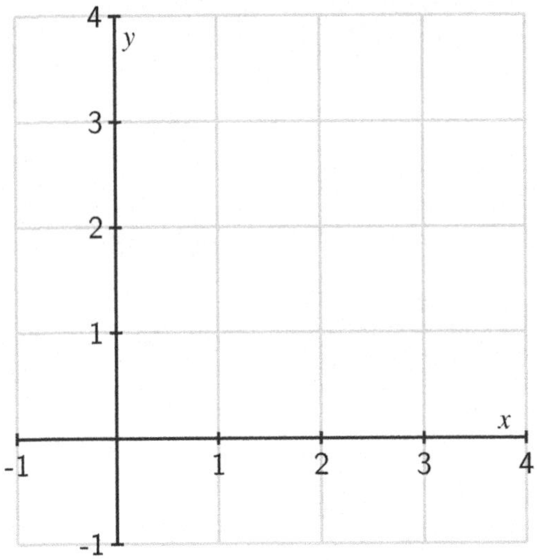

Figure 6.5.2 Plot the three data points here.

b. Remember that the equation of a line can be written as $b+mx=y$ where m is the slope and b is the y-intercept. We will try to find b and m so that the three points lie on the line.

   The first data point $(1,1)$ gives an equation for b and m. In particular, we know that when $x=1$, then $y=1$ so we have $b+m(1)=1$ or $b+m=1$. Use the other two data points to create a linear system describing m and b.

c. We have obtained a linear system having three equations, one from each data point, for the two unknowns b and m. Identify a matrix A and vector $\mathbf{b}$ so that the system has the form $A\mathbf{x}=\mathbf{b}$, where $\mathbf{x}=\begin{bmatrix} b \\ m \end{bmatrix}$.

   Notice that the unknown vector $\mathbf{x}=\begin{bmatrix} b \\ m \end{bmatrix}$ describes the line that we seek.

d. Is there a solution to this linear system? How does this question relate to your attempt to draw a line through the three points above?

e. Since this system is inconsistent, we know that $\mathbf{b}$ is not in the column space $\text{Col}(A)$. Find an orthogonal basis for $\text{Col}(A)$ and use it to find the orthogonal projection $\widehat{\mathbf{b}}$ of $\mathbf{b}$ onto $\text{Col}(A)$.

f. Since $\widehat{\mathbf{b}}$ is in $\text{Col}(A)$, the equation $A\mathbf{x}=\widehat{\mathbf{b}}$ is consistent. Find its solution $\mathbf{x}=\begin{bmatrix} b \\ m \end{bmatrix}$ and sketch the line $y=b+mx$ in Figure 6.5.2. We say that this is the line of best fit.

Activity 6.5.3 The rate at which a cricket chirps is related to the outdoor temperature, as reflected in some experimental data that we'll study in this activity. The chirp rate C is expressed in chirps per second while the temperature T is in degrees Fahrenheit. Evaluate the following cell to load the data:

```
base='https://raw.githubusercontent.com/davidaustinm/'
url=base+'ula_modules/master/orthogonality.py'
sage.repl.load.load(url, globals())
url=base+'ula_modules/master/data/crickets.csv'
df = pd.read_csv(url)
data = [vector(row) for row in df.values]
chirps = vector(df['Chirps'])
temps = vector(df['Temperature'])
print(df)
list_plot(data, color='blue', size=40, xmin=12, xmax=22, ymin=60, ymax=100)
```

Evaluating this cell also provides:

- the vectors `chirps` and `temps` formed from the columns of the dataset.
- the command `onesvec(n)`, which creates an n-dimensional vector whose entries are all one.
- Remember that you can form a matrix whose columns are the vectors `v1` and `v2` with `matrix([v1, v2]).T`.

We would like to represent this relationship by a linear function

$$\beta_0 + \beta_1 C = T.$$

a. Use the first data point $(C_1, T_1) = (20.0, 88.6)$ to write an equation involving β_0 and β_1.

b. Suppose that we represent the unknowns using a vector $\mathbf{x} = \begin{bmatrix} \beta_0 \\ \beta_1 \end{bmatrix}$. Use the 15 data points to create the matrix A and vector $\mathbf{b}$ so that the linear system $A\mathbf{x} = \mathbf{b}$ describes the unknown vector $\mathbf{x}$.

```

```

c. Write the normal equations $A^TA\widehat{\mathbf{x}} = A^T\mathbf{b}$; that is, find the matrix A^TA and the vector $A^T\mathbf{b}$.

d. Solve the normal equations to find $\widehat{\mathbf{x}}$, the least-squares approximate solution to the equation $A\mathbf{x} = \mathbf{b}$. Call your solution `xhat` since `x` has another meaning in Sage.

```

```

What are the values of β_0 and β_1 that you found?

e. If the chirp rate is 22 chirps per second, what is your prediction for the temperature?

You can plot the data and your line, assuming you called the solution `xhat`, using the cell below.

```
plot_model(xhat, data, domain=(12, 22))
```

Activity 6.5.4

a. Suppose we are interested in finding the least-squares approximate solution to the equation $A\mathbf{x} = \mathbf{b}$ and that we have the QR factorization $A = QR$. Explain why the least-squares approximation solution is given by solving

$$A\widehat{\mathbf{x}} = QQ^T\mathbf{b}$$

$$QR\widehat{\mathbf{x}} = QQ^T\mathbf{b}$$

b. Multiply both sides of the second expression by Q^T and explain why

$$R\widehat{\mathbf{x}} = Q^T\mathbf{b}.$$

Since R is upper triangular, this is a relatively simple equation to solve using back substitution, as we saw in Section 5.1. We will therefore write the least-squares approximate solution as

$$\widehat{\mathbf{x}} = R^{-1}Q^T\mathbf{b},$$

and put this to use in the following context.

c. Brozak's formula, which is used to calculate a person's body fat index BFI, is

$$BFI = 100\left(\frac{4.57}{\rho} - 4.142\right)$$

where ρ denotes a person's body density in grams per cubic centimeter. Obtaining an accurate measure of ρ is difficult, however, because it requires submerging the person in water and measuring the volume of water displaced. Instead, we will gather several other body measurements, which are more easily obtained, and use it to predict BFI.

For instance, suppose we take 10 patients and measure their weight w in pounds, height h in inches, abdomen a in centimeters, wrist circumference r in centimeters, neck circumference n in centimeters, and BFI. Evaluating the following cell loads and displays the data.

```
base='https://raw.githubusercontent.com/davidaustinm/'
url=base+'ula_modules/master/orthogonality.py'
sage.repl.load.load(url, globals())
url=base+'/ula_modules/master/data/bfi.csv'
df = pd.read_csv(url)
weight = vector(df['Weight'])
height = vector(df['Height'])
abdomen = vector(df['Abdomen'])
wrist = vector(df['Wrist'])
neck = vector(df['Neck'])
BFI = vector(df['BFI'])
print(df)
```

In addition, that cell provides:

(a) vectors `weight`, `height`, `abdomen`, `wrist`, `neck`, and `BFI` formed from the columns of the dataset.

(b) the command `onesvec(n)`, which returns an n-dimensional vector whose entries are all one.

(c) the command `QR(A)` that returns the QR factorization of A as `Q, R = QR(A)`.

(d) the command `demean(v)`, which returns the demeaned vector $\widetilde{\mathbf{v}}$.

We would like to find the linear function

$$\beta_0 + \beta_1 w + \beta_2 h + \beta_3 a + \beta_4 r + \beta_5 n = BFI$$

that best fits the data.

Use the first data point to write an equation for the parameters $\beta_0, \beta_1, \ldots, \beta_5$.

d. Describe the linear system $A\mathbf{x} = \mathbf{b}$ for these parameters. More specifically, describe how the matrix A and the vector $\mathbf{b}$ are formed.

e. Construct the matrix A and find its QR factorization in the cell below.

f. Find the least-squares approximate solution $\widehat{\mathbf{x}}$ by solving the equation $R\widehat{\mathbf{x}} = Q^T\mathbf{b}$. You may want to use `N(xhat)` to display a decimal approximation of the vector. What are the parameters $\beta_0, \beta_1, \ldots, \beta_5$ that best fit the data?

g. Find the coefficient of determination R^2 for your parameters. What does this imply about the quality of the fit?

h. Suppose a person's measurements are: weight 190, height 70, abdomen 90, wrist 18, and neck 35. Estimate this person's BFI.

Activity 6.5.5

a. Suppose that we have a small dataset containing the points $(0, 2)$, $(1, 1)$, $(2, 3)$, and $(3, 3)$, such as appear when the following cell is evaluated.

```
url='https://raw.githubusercontent.com/davidaustinm/'
url+='ula_modules/master/orthogonality.py'
sage.repl.load.load(url, globals())
data = [[0, 2], [1, 1], [2, 3], [3, 3]]
list_plot(data, color='blue', size=40)
```

In addition to loading and plotting the data, evaluating that cell provides the following commands:

- `Q, R = QR(A)` returns the QR factorization of A.
- `demean(v)` returns the demeaned vector $\widetilde{\mathbf{v}}$.

Let's fit a quadratic function of the form

$$\beta_0 + \beta_1 x + \beta_2 x^2 = y$$

to this dataset.

Write four equations, one for each data point, that describe the coefficients β_0, β_1, and β_2.

b. Express these four equations as a linear system $A\mathbf{x} = \mathbf{b}$ where $\mathbf{x} = \begin{bmatrix} \beta_0 \\ \beta_1 \\ \beta_2 \end{bmatrix}$.

Find the QR factorization of A and use it to find the least-squares approximate solution $\widehat{\mathbf{x}}$.

c. Use the parameters β_0, β_1, and β_2 that you found to write the quadratic function that fits the data. You can plot this function, along with the data, by entering your function in the place indicated below.

```
list_plot(data, color='blue', size=40) + plot( **your function here**,
0, 3, color='red')
```

d. What is your predicted y value when $x = 1.5$?

e. Find the coefficient of determination R^2 for the quadratic function. What does this say about the quality of the fit?

f. Now fit a cubic polynomial of the form

$$\beta_0 + \beta_1 x + \beta_2 x^2 + \beta_3 x^3 = y$$

to this dataset.

g. Find the coefficient of determination R^2 for the cubic function. What does this say about the quality of the fit?

h. What do you notice when you plot the cubic function along with the data? How does this reflect the value of R^2 that you found?

```
list_plot(data, color='blue', size=40) + plot( **your function here**,
0, 3, color='red')
```

Activity 6.5.6 This activity explores a dataset describing Arctic sea ice and that comes from Sustainability Math.[4]

Evaluating the cell below will plot the extent of Arctic sea ice, in millions of square kilometers, during the twelve months of 2012.

```
base='https://raw.githubusercontent.com/davidaustinm/'
url=base+'ula_modules/master/orthogonality.py'
sage.repl.load.load(url, globals())
url=base+'/ula_modules/master/data/sea_ice.csv'
df = pd.read_csv(url)
data = [vector([row[0], row[2]]) for row in df.values]
month = vector(df['Month'])
ice = vector(df['2012'])
print(df[['Month', '2012']])
list_plot(data, color='blue', size=40)
```

In addition, you have access to a few special variables and commands:

- `month` is the vector of month values and `ice` is the vector of sea ice values from the table above.
- `vandermonde(x, k)` constructs the Vandermonde matrix of degree k using the points in the vector `x`.
- `Q, R = QR(A)` provides the QR factorization of A.
- `demean(v)` returns the demeaned vector $\widetilde{\mathbf{v}}$.

a. Find the vector $\widehat{\mathbf{x}}$, the least-squares approximate solution to the linear system that results from fitting a degree 5 polynomial to the data.

b. If your result is stored in the variable `xhat`, you may plot the polynomial and the data together using the following cell.

```
plot_model(xhat, data)
```

c. Find the coefficient of determination R^2 for this polynomial fit.

d. Repeat these steps to fit a degree 8 polynomial to the data, plot the polynomial with the data, and find R^2.

e. Repeat one more time by fitting a degree 11 polynomial to the data, creating a plot, and finding R^2.

It's certainly true that higher degree polynomials fit the data better, as seen by the increasing values of R^2, but that's not always a good thing. For instance, when $k = 11$, you may notice that the graph of the polynomial wiggles a little more than we would expect. In this case, the polynomial is trying too hard to fit the data, which usually contains some uncertainty, especially if it's obtained from measurements. The error built in to the data is called *noise*, and its presence means that we shouldn't expect our polynomial to fit the data perfectly. When we choose a polynomial whose degree is too high, we give the noise too much weight in the model, which leads to some undesirable behavior, like the wiggles in the graph.

Fitting the data with a polynomial whose degree is too high is called *overfitting*, a phenomenon that can appear in many machine learning applications. Generally speaking, we would like to choose k large enough to capture the essential features of the data but not so large that we overfit and build the noise into the model. There are ways to determine the optimal value of k, but we won't pursue that here.

f. Choosing a reasonable value of k, estimate the extent of Arctic sea ice at month 6.5, roughly at the Summer Solstice.

7 *Singular value decompositions*

7.1 Symmetric matrices and variance

Preview Activity 7.1.1 This preview activity reminds us how a basis of eigenvectors can be used to relate a square matrix to a diagonal one.

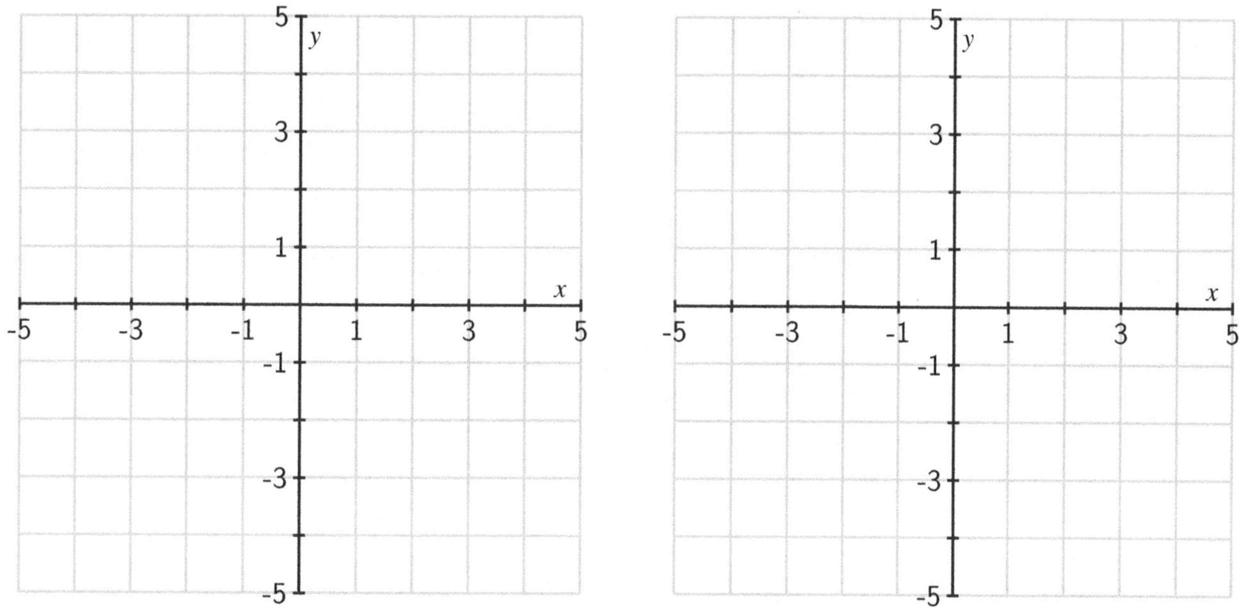

Figure 7.1.1 Use these plots to sketch the vectors requested in the preview activity.

a. Suppose that $D = \begin{bmatrix} 3 & 0 \\ 0 & -1 \end{bmatrix}$ and that $\mathbf{e}_1 = \begin{bmatrix} 1 \\ 0 \end{bmatrix}$ and $\mathbf{e}_2 = \begin{bmatrix} 0 \\ 1 \end{bmatrix}$.

1. Sketch the vectors $\mathbf{e}_1$ and $D\mathbf{e}_1$ on the left side of Figure 7.1.1.
2. Sketch the vectors $\mathbf{e}_2$ and $D\mathbf{e}_2$ on the left side of Figure 7.1.1.
3. Sketch the vectors $\mathbf{e}_1 + 2\mathbf{e}_2$ and $D(\mathbf{e}_1 + 2\mathbf{e}_2)$ on the left side.
4. Give a geometric description of the matrix transformation defined by D.

b. Now suppose we have vectors $\mathbf{v}_1 = \begin{bmatrix} 1 \\ 1 \end{bmatrix}$ and $\mathbf{v}_2 = \begin{bmatrix} -1 \\ 1 \end{bmatrix}$ and that A is a 2×2 matrix such that

$$A\mathbf{v}_1 = 3\mathbf{v}_1, \qquad A\mathbf{v}_2 = -\mathbf{v}_2.$$

That is, $\mathbf{v}_1$ and $\mathbf{v}_2$ are eigenvectors of A with associated eigenvalues 3 and -1.

1. Sketch the vectors $\mathbf{v}_1$ and $A\mathbf{v}_1$ on the right side of Figure 7.1.1.
2. Sketch the vectors $\mathbf{v}_2$ and $A\mathbf{v}_2$ on the right side of Figure 7.1.1.

3. Sketch the vectors $\mathbf{v}_1 + 2\mathbf{v}_2$ and $A(\mathbf{v}_1 + 2\mathbf{v}_2)$ on the right side.
4. Give a geometric description of the matrix transformation defined by A.

c. In what ways are the matrix transformations defined by D and A related to one another?

Activity 7.1.2 Remember that the Sage command `A.right_eigenmatrix()` attempts to find a basis for $\mathbb{R}^m$ consisting of eigenvectors of A. In particular, `D, P = A.right_eigenmatrix()` provides a diagonal matrix D constructed from the eigenvalues of A with the columns of P containing the associated eigenvectors.

a. For each of the following matrices, determine whether there is a basis for $\mathbb{R}^2$ consisting of eigenvectors of that matrix. When there is such a basis, form the matrices P and D and verify that the matrix equals PDP^{-1}.

   1. $\begin{bmatrix} 3 & -4 \\ 4 & 3 \end{bmatrix}$.
   2. $\begin{bmatrix} 1 & 1 \\ -1 & 3 \end{bmatrix}$.
   3. $\begin{bmatrix} 1 & 0 \\ -1 & 2 \end{bmatrix}$.
   4. $\begin{bmatrix} 9 & 2 \\ 2 & 6 \end{bmatrix}$.

b. For which of these examples is it possible to form an orthogonal basis for $\mathbb{R}^2$ consisting of eigenvectors?

c. For any such matrix A, find an orthonormal basis of eigenvectors and explain why $A = QDQ^{-1}$ where Q is an orthogonal matrix.

d. Finally, explain why $A = QDQ^T$ in this case.

e. When $A = QDQ^T$, what is the relationship between A and A^T?

Activity 7.1.3 Each of the following matrices is symmetric so the Spectral Theorem tells us that each is orthogonally diagonalizable. The point of this activity is to find an orthogonal diagonalization for each matrix.

To begin, find a basis for each eigenspace. Use this basis to find an orthogonal basis for each eigenspace and put these bases together to find an orthogonal basis for $\mathbb{R}^m$ consisting of eigenvectors. Use this basis to write an orthogonal diagonalization of the matrix.

a. $\begin{bmatrix} 0 & 2 \\ 2 & 3 \end{bmatrix}$.

b. $\begin{bmatrix} 4 & -2 & 14 \\ -2 & 19 & -16 \\ 14 & -16 & 13 \end{bmatrix}$.

c. $\begin{bmatrix} 5 & 4 & 2 \\ 4 & 5 & 2 \\ 2 & 2 & 2 \end{bmatrix}$.

d. Consider the matrix $A = B^T B$ where $B = \begin{bmatrix} 0 & 1 & 2 \\ 2 & 0 & 1 \end{bmatrix}$. Explain how we know that A is symmetric and then find an orthogonal diagonalization of A.

Activity 7.1.4 We'll begin with a set of three data points

$$\mathbf{d}_1 = \begin{bmatrix} 1 \\ 1 \end{bmatrix}, \quad \mathbf{d}_2 = \begin{bmatrix} 2 \\ 1 \end{bmatrix}, \quad \mathbf{d}_3 = \begin{bmatrix} 3 \\ 4 \end{bmatrix}.$$

a. Find the centroid, or mean, $\overline{\mathbf{d}} = \frac{1}{N}\sum_j \mathbf{d}_j$. Then plot the data points and their centroid in Figure 7.1.12.

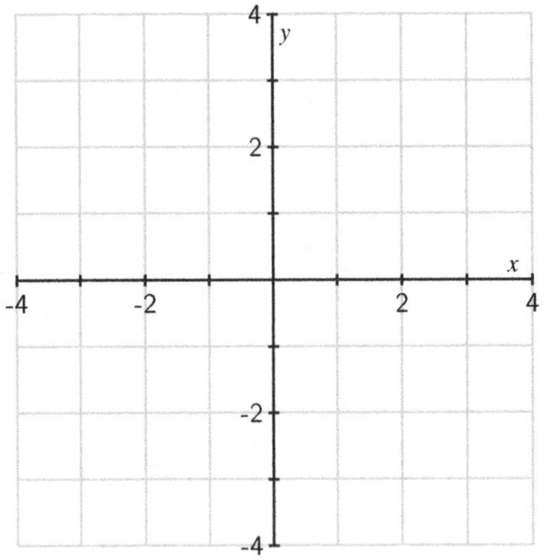

Figure 7.1.12 Plot the data points and their centroid here.

b. Notice that the centroid lies in the center of the data so the spread of the data will be measured by how far away the points are from the centroid. To simplify our calculations, find the demeaned data points

$$\widetilde{\mathbf{d}}_j = \mathbf{d}_j - \overline{\mathbf{d}}$$

and plot them in Figure 7.1.13.

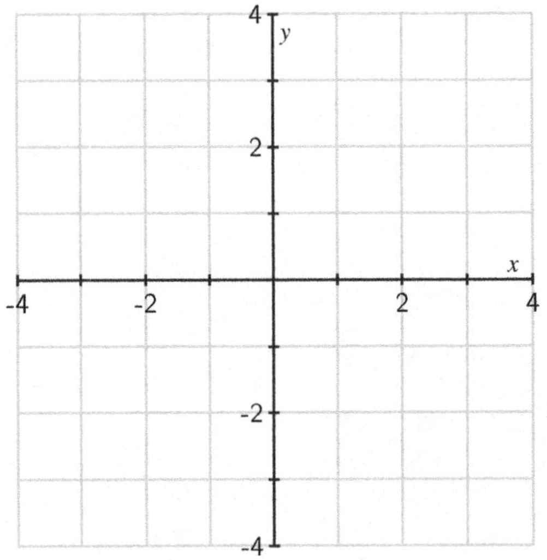

Figure 7.1.13 Plot the demeaned data points $\widetilde{\mathbf{d}}_j$ here.

c. Now that the data has been demeaned, we will define the total variance as the average of the squares of the distances from the origin; that is, the total variance is

$$V = \frac{1}{N}\sum_j |\widetilde{\mathbf{d}}_j|^2.$$

Find the total variance V for our set of three points.

d. Now plot the projections of the demeaned data onto the x and y axes using Figure 7.1.14 and find the variances V_x and V_y of the projected points.

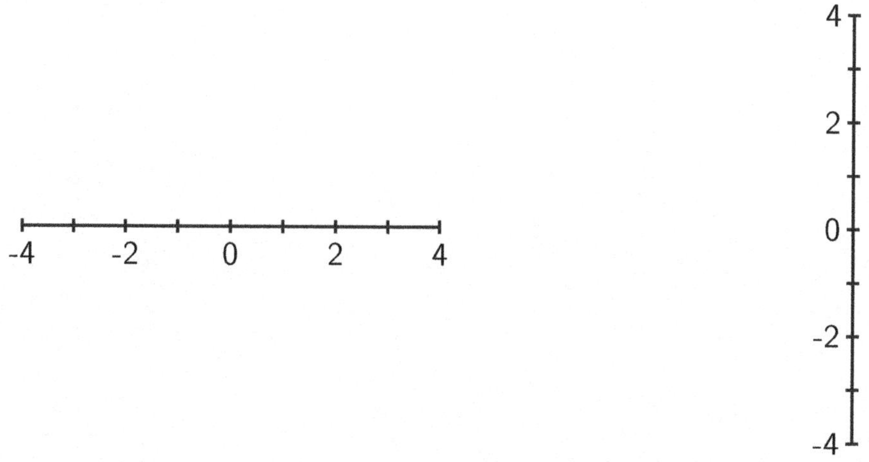

Figure 7.1.14 Plot the projections of the demeaned data onto the x and y axes.

e. Which of the variances, V_x and V_y, is larger and how does the plot of the projected points explain your response?

f. What do you notice about the relationship between V, V_x, and V_y? How does the Pythagorean theorem explain this relationship?

g. Plot the projections of the demeaned data points onto the lines defined by vectors $\mathbf{v}_1 = \begin{bmatrix} 1 \\ 1 \end{bmatrix}$ and $\mathbf{v}_2 = \begin{bmatrix} -1 \\ 1 \end{bmatrix}$ using Figure 7.1.15 and find the variances $V_{\mathbf{v}_1}$ and $V_{\mathbf{v}_2}$ of these projected points.

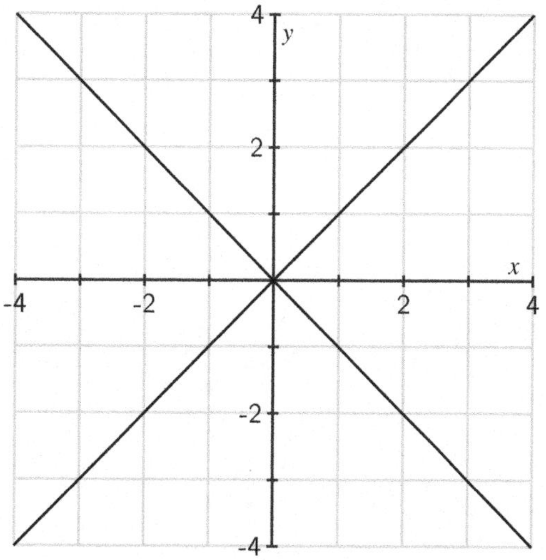

Figure 7.1.15 Plot the projections of the deameaned data onto the lines defined by $\mathbf{v}_1$ and $\mathbf{v}_2$.

h. What is the relationship between the total variance V and $V_{\mathbf{v}_1}$ and $V_{\mathbf{v}_2}$? How does the Pythagorean theorem explain your response?

Activity 7.1.5 Let's return to the dataset from the previous activity in which we have demeaned data points:

$$\widetilde{\mathbf{d}}_1 = \begin{bmatrix} -1 \\ -1 \end{bmatrix}, \qquad \widetilde{\mathbf{d}}_2 = \begin{bmatrix} 0 \\ -1 \end{bmatrix}, \qquad \widetilde{\mathbf{d}}_3 = \begin{bmatrix} 1 \\ 2 \end{bmatrix}.$$

Our goal is to compute the variance $V_{\mathbf{u}}$ in the direction defined by a unit vector $\mathbf{u}$.

To begin, form the demeaned data matrix

$$A = \begin{bmatrix} \widetilde{\mathbf{d}}_1 & \widetilde{\mathbf{d}}_2 & \widetilde{\mathbf{d}}_3 \end{bmatrix}$$

and suppose that $\mathbf{u}$ is a unit vector.

a. Write the vector $A^T\mathbf{u}$ in terms of the dot products $\widetilde{\mathbf{d}}_j \cdot \mathbf{u}$.

b. Explain why $V_{\mathbf{u}} = \frac{1}{3}|A^T\mathbf{u}|^2$.

c. Apply Proposition 7.1.10 to explain why

$$V_{\mathbf{u}} = \frac{1}{3}|A^T\mathbf{u}|^2 = \frac{1}{3}(A^T\mathbf{u}) \cdot (A^T\mathbf{u}) = \mathbf{u}^T\left(\frac{1}{3}AA^T\right)\mathbf{u} = \mathbf{u} \cdot \left(\frac{1}{3}AA^T\right)\mathbf{u} =$$

d. In general, the matrix $C = \frac{1}{N}AA^T$ is called the *covariance* matrix of the dataset, and it is useful because the variance $V_{\mathbf{u}} = \mathbf{u} \cdot (C\mathbf{u})$, as we have just seen. Find the matrix C for our dataset with three points.

e. Use the covariance matrix to find the variance $V_{\mathbf{u}_1}$ when $\mathbf{u}_1 = \begin{bmatrix} 1/\sqrt{5} \\ 2/\sqrt{5} \end{bmatrix}$.

f. Use the covariance matrix to find the variance $V_{\mathbf{u}_2}$ when $\mathbf{u}_2 = \begin{bmatrix} -2/\sqrt{5} \\ 1/\sqrt{5} \end{bmatrix}$. Since $\mathbf{u}_1$ and $\mathbf{u}_2$ are orthogonal, verify that the sum of $V_{\mathbf{u}_1}$ and $V_{\mathbf{u}_2}$ gives the total variance.

g. Explain why the covariance matrix C is a symmetric matrix.

Activity 7.1.6

a. Evaluating the following Sage cell loads a dataset consisting of 100 demeaned data points and provides a plot of them. It also provides the demeaned data matrix A.

```
import pandas as pd
url='https://raw.githubusercontent.com/davidaustinm/'
url+='ula_modules/master/data/variance-data.csv'
df=pd.read_csv(url, header=None)
data = [vector(row) for row in df.values]
A = matrix(data).T
list_plot(data, size=20, color='blue', aspect_ratio=1)
```

What is the shape of the covariance matrix C? Find C and verify your response.

```
```

b. By visually inspecting the data, determine which is larger, V_x or V_y. Then compute both of these quantities to verify your response.

c. What is the total variance V?

d. In approximately what direction is the variance greatest? Choose a reasonable vector $\mathbf{u}$ that points in approximately that direction and find $V_{\mathbf{u}}$.

e. In approximately what direction is the variance smallest? Choose a reasonable vector $\mathbf{w}$ that points in approximately that direction and find $V_{\mathbf{w}}$.

f. How are the directions $\mathbf{u}$ and $\mathbf{w}$ in the last two parts of this problem related to one another? Why does this relationship hold?

7.2 Quadratic forms

Preview Activity 7.2.1 Let's begin by looking at an example. Suppose we have three data points that form the demeaned data matrix

$$A = \begin{bmatrix} 2 & 1 & -3 \\ 1 & 2 & -3 \end{bmatrix}$$

a. Plot the demeaned data points in Figure 7.2.1. In which direction does the variance appear to be largest and in which does it appear to be smallest?

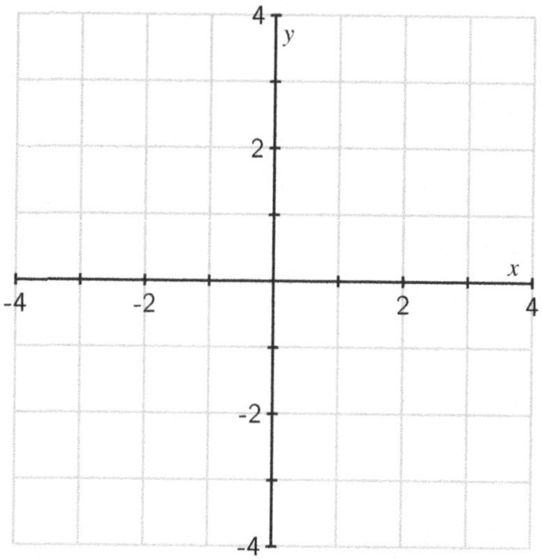

Figure 7.2.1 Use this coordinate grid to plot the demeaned data points.

b. Construct the covariance matrix C and determine the variance in the direction of $\begin{bmatrix} 1 \\ 1 \end{bmatrix}$ and the variance in the direction of $\begin{bmatrix} -1 \\ 1 \end{bmatrix}$.

c. What is the total variance of this dataset?

d. Generally speaking, if C is the covariance matrix of a dataset and $\mathbf{u}$ is an eigenvector of C having unit length and with associated eigenvalue λ, what is $V_{\mathbf{u}}$?

Activity 7.2.2 Let's look at some more examples of quadratic forms.

a. Consider the symmetric matrix $D = \begin{bmatrix} 3 & 0 \\ 0 & -1 \end{bmatrix}$. Write the quadratic form $q_D(\mathbf{x})$ defined by D in terms of the components of $\mathbf{x} = \begin{bmatrix} x_1 \\ x_2 \end{bmatrix}$. What is the value of $q_D\left(\begin{bmatrix} 2 \\ -4 \end{bmatrix}\right)$?

b. Given the symmetric matrix $A = \begin{bmatrix} 2 & 5 \\ 5 & -3 \end{bmatrix}$, write the quadratic form $q_A(\mathbf{x})$ and evaluate $q_A\left(\begin{bmatrix} 2 \\ -1 \end{bmatrix}\right)$.

c. Suppose that $q\left(\begin{bmatrix} x_1 \\ x_2 \end{bmatrix}\right) = 3x_1^2 - 4x_1x_2 + 4x_2^2$. Find a symmetric matrix A such that q is the quadratic form defined by A.

d. Suppose that q is a quadratic form and that $q(\mathbf{x}) = 3$. What is $q(2\mathbf{x})$? $q(-\mathbf{x})$? $q(10\mathbf{x})$?

e. Suppose that A is a symmetric matrix and $q_A(\mathbf{x})$ is the quadratic form defined by A. Suppose that $\mathbf{x}$ is an eigenvector of A with associated eigenvalue -4 and with length 7. What is $q_A(\mathbf{x})$?

Activity 7.2.3 We can gain some intuition about this problem by graphing the quadratic form and paying particular attention to the unit vectors.

a. Evaluating the following cell defines the matrix $D = \begin{bmatrix} 3 & 0 \\ 0 & -1 \end{bmatrix}$ and displays the graph of the associated quadratic form $q_D(\mathbf{x})$. In addition, the points corresponding to vectors $\mathbf{u}$ with unit length are displayed as a curve.

```
url='https://raw.githubusercontent.com/davidaustinm/'
url+='ula_modules/master/quad_plot.py'
sage.repl.load.load(url, globals())

## We define our matrix here
A = matrix(2, 2, [3, 0, 0, -1])

quad_plot(A)
```

Notice that the matrix D is diagonal. In which directions does the quadratic form have its maximum and minimum values?

b. Write the quadratic form q_D associated to D. What is the value of $q_D\left(\begin{bmatrix} 1 \\ 0 \end{bmatrix}\right)$? What is the value of $q_D\left(\begin{bmatrix} 0 \\ 1 \end{bmatrix}\right)$?

c. Consider a unit vector $\mathbf{u} = \begin{bmatrix} u_1 \\ u_2 \end{bmatrix}$ so that $u_1^2 + u_2^2 = 1$, an expression we can rewrite as $u_1^2 = 1 - u_2^2$. Write the quadratic form $q_D(\mathbf{u})$ and replace u_1^2 by $1 - u_2^2$. Now explain why the maximum of $q_D(\mathbf{u})$ is 3. In which direction does the maximum occur? Does this agree with what you observed from the graph above?

d. Write the quadratic form $q_D(\mathbf{u})$ and replace u_2^2 by $1 - u_1^2$. What is the minimum value of $q_D(\mathbf{u})$ and in which direction does the minimum occur?

e. Use the previous Sage cell to change the matrix to $A = \begin{bmatrix} 1 & 2 \\ 2 & 1 \end{bmatrix}$ and display the graph of the quadratic form $q_A(\mathbf{x}) = \mathbf{x} \cdot (A\mathbf{x})$. Determine the directions in which the maximum and minimum occur?

f. Remember that $A = \begin{bmatrix} 1 & 2 \\ 2 & 1 \end{bmatrix}$ is symmetric so that $A = QDQ^T$ where D is the diagonal matrix above and Q is the orthogonal matrix that rotates vectors by 45°. Notice that

$$q_A(\mathbf{u}) = \mathbf{u} \cdot (A\mathbf{u}) = \mathbf{u} \cdot (QDQ^T\mathbf{u}) = (Q^T\mathbf{u}) \cdot (DQ^T\mathbf{u}) = q_D(\mathbf{v})$$

where $\mathbf{v} = Q^T\mathbf{u}$. That is, we have $q_A(\mathbf{u}) = q_D(\mathbf{v})$.

Explain why $\mathbf{v} = Q^T\mathbf{u}$ is also a unit vector; that is, explain why

$$|\mathbf{v}|^2 = |Q^T\mathbf{u}|^2 = (Q^T\mathbf{u}) \cdot (Q^T\mathbf{u}) = 1.$$

g. Using the fact that $q_A(\mathbf{u}) = q_D(\mathbf{v})$, explain how we now know the maximum value of $q_A(\mathbf{u})$ is 3 and determine the direction in which it occurs. Also, determine the minimum value of $q_A(\mathbf{u})$ and determine the direction in which it occurs.

Activity 7.2.4 This activity explores the relationship between the eigenvalues of a symmetric matrix and its definiteness.

a. Consider the diagonal matrix $D = \begin{bmatrix} 4 & 0 \\ 0 & 2 \end{bmatrix}$ and write its quadratic form $q_D(\mathbf{x})$ in terms of the components of $\mathbf{x} = \begin{bmatrix} x_1 \\ x_2 \end{bmatrix}$. How does this help you decide whether D is positive definite or not?

b. Now consider $D = \begin{bmatrix} 4 & 0 \\ 0 & 0 \end{bmatrix}$ and write its quadratic form $q_D(\mathbf{x})$ in terms of x_1 and x_2. What can you say about the definiteness of D?

c. If D is a diagonal matrix, what condition on the diagonal entries guarantee that D is

1. positive definite?
2. positive semidefinite?
3. negative definite?
4. negative semidefinite?
5. indefinite?

d. Suppose that A is a symmetric matrix with eigenvalues 4 and 2 so that $A = QDQ^T$ where $D = \begin{bmatrix} 4 & 0 \\ 0 & 2 \end{bmatrix}$. If $\mathbf{y} = Q^T\mathbf{x}$, then we have $q_A(\mathbf{x}) = q_D(\mathbf{y})$. Explain why this tells us that A is positive definite.

e. Suppose that A is a symmetric matrix with eigenvalues 4 and 0. What can you say about the definiteness of A in this case?

f. What condition on the eigenvalues of a symmetric matrix A guarantees that A is

1. positive definite?
2. positive semidefinite?
3. negative definite?
4. negative semidefinite?
5. indefinite?

Activity 7.2.5 Let's explore how our understanding of quadratic forms helps us determine the behavior of a function f near a critical point.

a. Consider the function $f(x,y) = 2x^3 - 6xy + 3y^2$. Find the partial derivatives f_x and f_y and use these expressions to determine the critical points of f.

b. Evaluate the second partial derivatives f_{xx}, f_{xy}, and f_{yy}.

c. Let's first consider the critical point $(1,1)$. Use the quadratic approximation as written above to find an expression approximating f near the critical point.

d. Using the vector $\mathbf{w} = \begin{bmatrix} x-1 \\ y-1 \end{bmatrix}$, rewrite your approximation as

$$f(x,y) \approx f(1,1) + q_A(\mathbf{w})$$

for some matrix A. What is the matrix A in this case?

e. Find the eigenvalues of A. What can you conclude about the definiteness of A?

f. Recall that (x_0, y_0) is a local minimum for f if $f(x,y) > f(x_0, y_0)$ for nearby points (x,y). Explain why our understanding of the eigenvalues of A shows that $(1,1)$ is a local minimum for f.

```
plot3d(2*x^3 - 6*x*y + 3*y^2, (x, -2,2), (y,-2,2))
```

7.3 Principal Component Analysis

Preview Activity 7.3.1 We will begin by recalling our earlier discussion of variance. Suppose we have a dataset that leads to the covariance matrix

$$C = \begin{bmatrix} 7 & -4 \\ -4 & 13 \end{bmatrix}.$$

a. Suppose that $\mathbf{u}$ is a unit eigenvector of C with eigenvalue λ. What is the variance $V_{\mathbf{u}}$ in the $\mathbf{u}$ direction?

b. Find an orthogonal diagonalization of C.

c. What is the total variance?

d. In which direction is the variance greatest and what is the variance in this direction? If we project the data onto this line, how much variance is lost?

e. In which direction is the variance smallest and how is this direction related to the direction of maximum variance?

Activity 7.3.2 Suppose that we work with a dataset having 100 five-dimensional data points. The demeaned data matrix A is therefore 5×100 and leads to the covariance matrix $C = \frac{1}{100} AA^T$, which is a 5×5 matrix. Because C is symmetric, the Spectral Theorem tells us it is orthogonally diagonalizable so suppose that $C = QDQ^T$ where

$$Q = \begin{bmatrix} \mathbf{u}_1 & \mathbf{u}_2 & \mathbf{u}_3 & \mathbf{u}_4 & \mathbf{u}_5 \end{bmatrix}, \qquad D = \begin{bmatrix} 13 & 0 & 0 & 0 & 0 \\ 0 & 10 & 0 & 0 & 0 \\ 0 & 0 & 2 & 0 & 0 \\ 0 & 0 & 0 & 0 & 0 \\ 0 & 0 & 0 & 0 & 0 \end{bmatrix}.$$

a. What is $V_{\mathbf{u}_2}$, the variance in the $\mathbf{u}_2$ direction?

b. Find the variance of the data projected onto the line defined by $\mathbf{u}_4$. What does this say about the data?

c. What is the total variance of the data?

d. Consider the 2-dimensional subspace spanned by $\mathbf{u}_1$ and $\mathbf{u}_2$. If we project the data onto this subspace, what fraction of the total variance is represented by the variance of the projected data?

e. How does this question change if we project onto the 3-dimensional subspace spanned by $\mathbf{u}_1$, $\mathbf{u}_2$, and $\mathbf{u}_3$?

f. What does this tell us about the data?

Activity 7.3.3 We will work here with a dataset having 100 3-dimensional demeaned data points. Evaluating the following cell will plot those data points and define the demeaned data matrix A whose shape is 3×100.

```
url='https://raw.githubusercontent.com/davidaustinm/'
url+='ula_modules/master/pca_demo.py'
sage.repl.load.load(url, globals())
```

Notice that the data appears to cluster around a plane though it does not seem to be wholly contained within that plane.

a. Use the matrix A to construct the covariance matrix C. Then determine the variance in the direction of $\mathbf{u} = \begin{bmatrix} 1/3 \\ 2/3 \\ 2/3 \end{bmatrix}$?

b. Find the eigenvalues of C and determine the total variance.

   Notice that Sage does not necessarily sort the eigenvalues in decreasing order.

c. Use the `right_eigenmatrix()` command to find the eigenvectors of C. Remembering that the Sage command `B.column(1)` retrieves the vector represented by the second column of `B`, define vectors `u1`, `u2`, and `u3` representing the three principal components in order of decreasing eigenvalues. How can you check if these vectors are an orthonormal basis for $\mathbb{R}^3$?

d. What fraction of the total variance is retained by projecting the data onto W_1, the subspace spanned by $\mathbf{u}_1$? What fraction of the total variance is retained by projecting onto W_2, the subspace spanned by $\mathbf{u}_1$ and $\mathbf{u}_2$? What fraction of the total variance do we lose by projecting onto W_2?

e. If we project a data point $\mathbf{x}$ onto W_2, the Projection Formula tells us we obtain

$$\widehat{\mathbf{x}} = (\mathbf{u}_1 \cdot \mathbf{x})\mathbf{u}_1 + (\mathbf{u}_2 \cdot \mathbf{x})\mathbf{u}_2.$$

   Rather than viewing the projected data in $\mathbb{R}^3$, we will record the coordinates of $\widehat{\mathbf{x}}$ in the basis defined by $\mathbf{u}_1$ and $\mathbf{u}_2$; that is, we will record the coordinates

$$\begin{bmatrix} \mathbf{u}_1 \cdot \mathbf{x} \\ \mathbf{u}_2 \cdot \mathbf{x} \end{bmatrix}.$$

   Construct the matrix Q so that $Q^T\mathbf{x} = \begin{bmatrix} \mathbf{u}_1 \cdot \mathbf{x} \\ \mathbf{u}_2 \cdot \mathbf{x} \end{bmatrix}$.

f. Since each column of A represents a data point, the matrix Q^TA represents the coordinates of the projected data points. Evaluating the following cell will plot those projected data points.

```
pca_plot(Q.T*A)
```

   Notice how this plot enables us to view the data as if it were two-dimensional. Why is this plot wider than it is tall?

Activity 7.3.4 The next cell will load a dataset describing the average consumption of various food groups for citizens in each of the four nations of the United Kingdom. The units for each entry are grams per person per week.

```
import pandas as pd
url='https://raw.githubusercontent.com/davidaustinm/'
url+='ula_modules/master/data/uk-diet.csv'
df = pd.read_csv(url, index_col=0)
data_mean = vector(df.T.mean())
A = matrix([vector(row) for row in (df.T-df.T.mean()).values]).T
df
```

We will view this as a dataset consisting of four points in $\mathbb{R}^{17}$. As such, it is impossible to visualize and studying the numbers themselves doesn't lead to much insight.

In addition to loading the data, evaluating the cell above created a vector `data_mean`, which is the mean of the four data points, and `A`, the 17×4 matrix of demeaned data.

a. What is the average consumption of Beverages across the four nations?

b. Find the covariance matrix C and its eigenvalues. Because there are four points in $\mathbb{R}^{17}$ whose mean is zero, there are only three nonzero eigenvalues.

c. For what percentage of the total variance does the first principal component account?

d. Find the first principal component $\mathbf{u}_1$ and project the four demeaned data points onto the line defined by $\mathbf{u}_1$. Plot those points on Figure 7.3.2

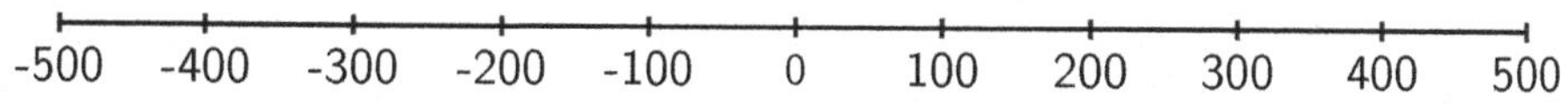

Figure 7.3.2 A plot of the demeaned data projected onto the first principal component.

e. For what percentage of the total variance do the first two principal components account?

f. Find the coordinates of the demeaned data points projected onto W_2, the two-dimensional subspace of $\mathbb{R}^{17}$ spanned by the first two principal components.

Plot these coordinates in Figure 7.3.3.

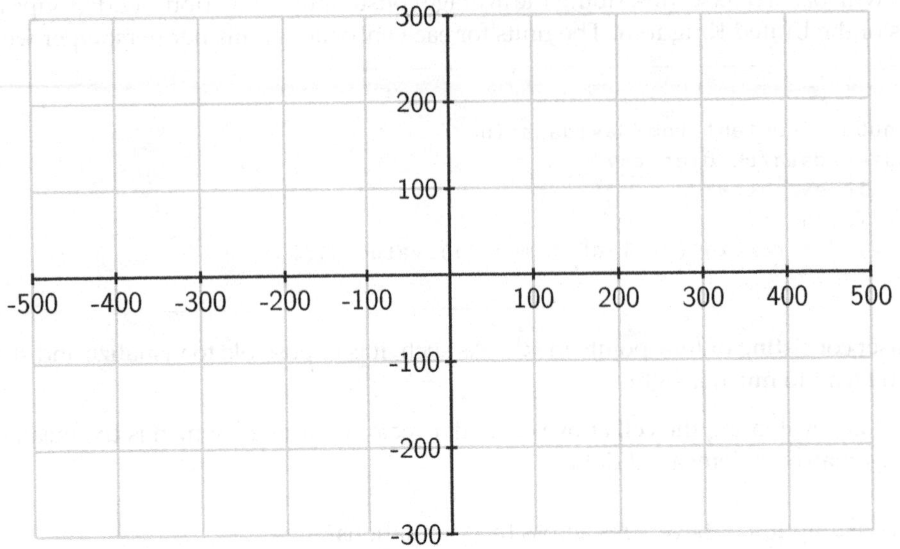

Figure 7.3.3 The coordinates of the demeaned data points projected onto the first two principal components.

g. What information do these plots reveal that is not clear from consideration of the original data points?

h. Study the first principal component $\mathbf{u}_1$ and find the first component of $\mathbf{u}_1$, which corresponds to the dietary category Alcoholic Drinks. (To do this, you may wish to use `N(u1, digits=2)` for a result that's easier to read.) If a data point lies on the far right side of the plot in Figure 7.3.3, what does it mean about that nation's consumption of Alcoholic Drinks?

Activity 7.3.5 In this activity, we'll look at a well-known dataset[5] that describes 150 irises representing three species of iris: Iris setosa, Iris versicolor, and Iris virginica. For each flower, the length and width of its sepal and the length and width of its petal, all in centimeters, are recorded.

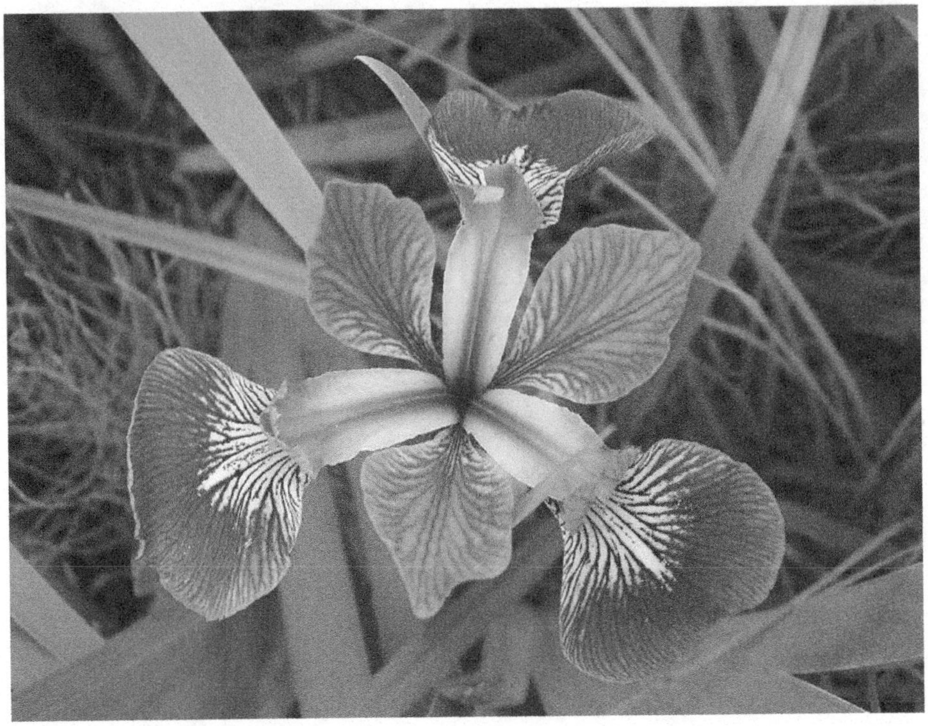

Figure 7.3.8 One of the three species, iris versicolor, represented in the dataset showing three shorter petals and three longer sepals. (Source: Wikipedia[6], License: GNU Free Documetation License[7])

Evaluating the following cell will load the dataset, which consists of 150 points in $\mathbb{R}^4$. In addition, we have a vector `data_mean`, a four-dimensional vector holding the mean of the data points, and `A`, the 4×150 demeaned data matrix.

```
url='https://raw.githubusercontent.com/davidaustinm/'
url+='ula_modules/master/pca_iris.py'
sage.repl.load.load(url, globals())
df.T
```

Since the data is four-dimensional, we are not able to visualize it. Of course, we could forget about two of the measurements and plot the 150 points represented by their, say, sepal length and sepal width.

```
sepal_plot()
```

a. What is the mean sepal width?

b. Find the covariance matrix C and its eigenvalues.

c. Find the fraction of variance for which the first two principal components account.

d. Construct the first two principal components $\mathbf{u}_1$ and $\mathbf{u}_2$ along with the matrix Q whose columns are $\mathbf{u}_1$ and $\mathbf{u}_2$.

e. As we have seen, the columns of the matrix Q^TA hold the coordinates of the demeaned data points after projecting onto W_2, the subspace spanned by the first two principal components. Evaluating the following cell shows a plot of these coordinates.

```
pca_plot(Q.T*A)
```

Suppose we have a flower whose coordinates in this plane are $(-2.5, -0.75)$. To what species does this iris most likely belong? Find an estimate of the sepal length, sepal width, petal length, and petal width for this flower.

f. Suppose you have an iris, but you only know that its sepal length is 5.65 cm and its sepal width is 2.75 cm. Knowing only these two measurements, determine the coordinates (c_1, c_2) in the plane where this iris lies. To what species does this iris most likely belong? Now estimate the petal length and petal width of this iris.

```
```

g. Suppose you find another iris whose sepal width is 3.2 cm and whose petal width is 2.2 cm. Find the coordinates (c_1, c_2) of this iris and determine the species to which it most likely belongs. Also, estimate the sepal length and the petal length.

```
```

7.4 Singular Value Decompositions

Preview Activity 7.4.1 Let's review orthogonal diagonalizations and quadratic forms as our understanding of singular value decompositions will rely on them.

a. Suppose that A is any matrix. Explain why the matrix $G = A^T A$ is symmetric.

b. Suppose that $A = \begin{bmatrix} 1 & 2 \\ -2 & -1 \end{bmatrix}$. Find the matrix $G = A^T A$ and write out the quadratic form $q_G\left(\begin{bmatrix} x_1 \\ x_2 \end{bmatrix}\right)$ as a function of x_1 and x_2.

c. What is the maximum value of $q_G(\mathbf{x})$ and in which direction does it occur?

d. What is the minimum value of $q_G(\mathbf{x})$ and in which direction does it occur?

e. What is the geometric relationship between the directions in which the maximum and minimum values occur?

Activity 7.4.2 The following interactive figure will help us explore singular values and vectors geometrically before we begin a more algebraic approach.

There is an interactive diagram, available at `gvsu.edu/s/0YE`, that accompanies this activity.

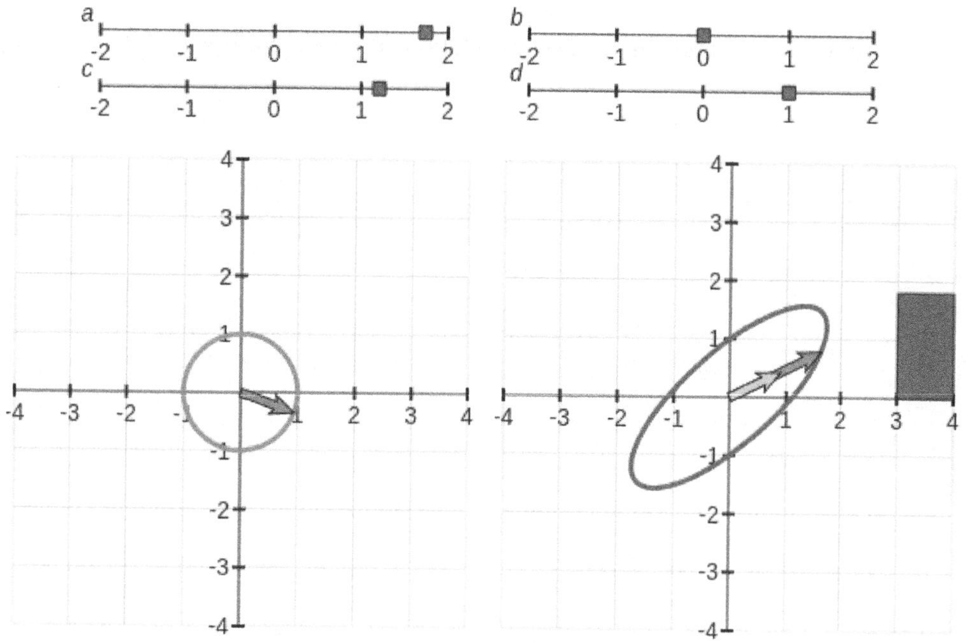

Figure 7.4.1 Singular values, right singular vectors and left singular vectors

Select the matrix $A = \begin{bmatrix} 1 & 2 \\ -2 & -1 \end{bmatrix}$. As we vary the vector $\mathbf{x}$, we see the vector $A\mathbf{x}$ on the right in gray while the height of the blue bar to the right tells us $l_A(\mathbf{x}) = |A\mathbf{x}|$.

a. The first *singular value* σ_1 is the maximum value of $l_A(\mathbf{x})$ and an associated *right singular vector* $\mathbf{v}_1$ is a unit vector describing a direction in which this maximum occurs.

   Use the diagram to find the first singular value σ_1 and an associated right singular vector $\mathbf{v}_1$.

b. The second singular value σ_2 is the minimum value of $l_A(\mathbf{x})$ and an associated right singular vector $\mathbf{v}_2$ is a unit vector describing a direction in which this minimum occurs.

   Use the diagram to find the second singular value σ_2 and an associated right singular vector $\mathbf{v}_2$.

c. Here's how we can find the right singular values and vectors without using the diagram. Remember that $l_A(\mathbf{x}) = \sqrt{q_G(\mathbf{x})}$ where $G = A^TA$ is the Gram matrix associated to A. Since G is symmetric, it is orthogonally diagonalizable. Find G and an orthogonal diagonalization of it.

   What is the maximum value of the quadratic form $q_G(\mathbf{x})$ among all unit vectors and in which direction does it occur? What is the minimum value of $q_G(\mathbf{x})$ and in which direction does it occur?

d. Because $l_A(\mathbf{x}) = \sqrt{q_G(\mathbf{x})}$, the first singular value σ_1 will be the square root of the maximum value of $q_G(\mathbf{x})$ and σ_2 the square root of the minimum. Verify that the singular values that you found from the diagram are the square roots of the maximum and minimum values of $q_G(\mathbf{x})$.

e. Verify that the right singular vectors $\mathbf{v}_1$ and $\mathbf{v}_2$ that you found from the diagram are the directions in which the maximum and minimum values occur.

f. Finally, we introduce the *left singular vectors* $\mathbf{u}_1$ and $\mathbf{u}_2$ by requiring that $A\mathbf{v}_1 = \sigma_1\mathbf{u}_1$ and $A\mathbf{v}_2 = \sigma_2\mathbf{u}_2$. Find the two left singular vectors.

g. Form the matrices

$$U = \begin{bmatrix} \mathbf{u}_1 & \mathbf{u}_2 \end{bmatrix}, \qquad \Sigma = \begin{bmatrix} \sigma_1 & 0 \\ 0 & \sigma_2 \end{bmatrix}, \qquad V = \begin{bmatrix} \mathbf{v}_1 & \mathbf{v}_2 \end{bmatrix}$$

and explain why $AV = U\Sigma$.

h. Finally, explain why $A = U\Sigma V^T$ and verify that this relationship holds for this specific example.

Activity 7.4.3 In this activity, we will construct the singular value decomposition of $A = \begin{bmatrix} 1 & 0 & -1 \\ 1 & 1 & 1 \end{bmatrix}$. Notice that this matrix is not square so there are no eigenvalues and eigenvectors associated to it.

a. Construct the Gram matrix $G = A^T A$ and find an orthogonal diagonalization of it.

b. Identify the singular values of A and the right singular vectors $\mathbf{v}_1$, $\mathbf{v}_2$, and $\mathbf{v}_3$. What is the dimension of these vectors? How many nonzero singular values are there?

c. Find the left singular vectors $\mathbf{u}_1$ and $\mathbf{u}_2$ using the fact that $A\mathbf{v}_i = \sigma_i \mathbf{u}_i$. What is the dimension of these vectors? What happens if you try to find a third left singular vector $\mathbf{u}_3$ in this way?

d. As before, form the orthogonal matrices U and V from the left and right singular vectors. What are the shapes of U and V? How do these shapes relate to the number of rows and columns of A?

e. Now form Σ so that it has the same shape as A:

$$\Sigma = \begin{bmatrix} \sigma_1 & 0 & 0 \\ 0 & \sigma_2 & 0 \end{bmatrix}$$

and verify that $A = U\Sigma V^T$.

f. How can you use this singular value decomposition of $A = U\Sigma V^T$ to easily find a singular value decomposition of $A^T = \begin{bmatrix} 1 & 1 \\ 0 & 1 \\ -1 & 1 \end{bmatrix}$?

Activity 7.4.4 Let's suppose that a matrix A has a singular value decomposition $A = U\Sigma V^T$ where

$$U = \begin{bmatrix} \mathbf{u}_1 & \mathbf{u}_2 & \mathbf{u}_3 & \mathbf{u}_4 \end{bmatrix}, \quad \Sigma = \begin{bmatrix} 20 & 0 & 0 \\ 0 & 5 & 0 \\ 0 & 0 & 0 \\ 0 & 0 & 0 \end{bmatrix}, \quad V = \begin{bmatrix} \mathbf{v}_1 & \mathbf{v}_2 & \mathbf{v}_3 \end{bmatrix}.$$

a. What is the shape of A; that is, how many rows and columns does A have?

b. Suppose we write a three-dimensional vector $\mathbf{x}$ as a linear combination of right singular vectors:

$$\mathbf{x} = c_1\mathbf{v}_1 + c_2\mathbf{v}_2 + c_3\mathbf{v}_3.$$

We would like to find an expression for $A\mathbf{x}$.

To begin, $V^T\mathbf{x} = \begin{bmatrix} \mathbf{v}_1 \cdot \mathbf{x} \\ \mathbf{v}_2 \cdot \mathbf{x} \\ \mathbf{v}_3 \cdot \mathbf{x} \end{bmatrix} = \begin{bmatrix} c_1 \\ c_2 \\ c_3 \end{bmatrix}$.

Now $\Sigma V^T\mathbf{x} = \begin{bmatrix} 20 & 0 & 0 \\ 0 & 5 & 0 \\ 0 & 0 & 0 \\ 0 & 0 & 0 \end{bmatrix} \begin{bmatrix} c_1 \\ c_2 \\ c_3 \end{bmatrix} = \begin{bmatrix} 20c_1 \\ 5c_2 \\ 0 \\ 0 \end{bmatrix}$.

And finally, $A\mathbf{x} = U\Sigma V^T\mathbf{x} = \begin{bmatrix} \mathbf{u}_1 & \mathbf{u}_2 & \mathbf{u}_3 & \mathbf{u}_4 \end{bmatrix} \begin{bmatrix} 20c_1 \\ 5c_2 \\ 0 \\ 0 \end{bmatrix} = 20c_1\mathbf{u}_1 + 5c_2\mathbf{u}_2$.

To summarize, we have $A\mathbf{x} = 20c_1\mathbf{u}_1 + 5c_2\mathbf{u}_2$.

What condition on c_1, c_2, and c_3 must be satisfied if $\mathbf{x}$ is a solution to the equation $A\mathbf{x} = 40\mathbf{u}_1 + 20\mathbf{u}_2$? Is there a unique solution or infinitely many?

c. Remembering that $\mathbf{u}_1$ and $\mathbf{u}_2$ are linearly independent, what condition on c_1, c_2, and c_3 must be satisfied if $A\mathbf{x} = \mathbf{0}$?

d. How do the right singular vectors $\mathbf{v}_i$ provide a basis for $\text{Nul}(A)$, the subspace of solutions to the equation $A\mathbf{x} = \mathbf{0}$?

e. Remember that $\mathbf{b}$ is in $\text{Col}(A)$ if the equation $A\mathbf{x} = \mathbf{b}$ is consistent, which means that

$$A\mathbf{x} = 20c_1\mathbf{u}_1 + 5c_2\mathbf{u}_2 = \mathbf{b}$$

for some coefficients c_1 and c_2. How do the left singular vectors $\mathbf{u}_i$ provide an orthonormal basis for $\text{Col}(A)$?

f. Remember that $\text{rank}(A)$ is the dimension of the column space. What is $\text{rank}(A)$ and how do the number of nonzero singular values determine $\text{rank}(A)$?

Activity 7.4.5 Suppose we have a singular value decomposition $A = U\Sigma V^T$ where

$$U = \begin{bmatrix} \mathbf{u}_1 & \mathbf{u}_2 & \mathbf{u}_3 & \mathbf{u}_4 \end{bmatrix}, \qquad \Sigma = \begin{bmatrix} 18 & 0 & 0 \\ 0 & 4 & 0 \\ 0 & 0 & 0 \\ 0 & 0 & 0 \end{bmatrix}, \qquad V = \begin{bmatrix} \mathbf{v}_1 & \mathbf{v}_2 & \mathbf{v}_3 \end{bmatrix}.$$

a. What is the shape of A? What is $\text{rank}(A)$?

b. Identify bases for $\text{Col}(A)$ and $\text{Col}(A^T)$.

c. Explain why

$$U\Sigma = \begin{bmatrix} \mathbf{u}_1 & \mathbf{u}_2 \end{bmatrix} \begin{bmatrix} 18 & 0 & 0 \\ 0 & 4 & 0 \end{bmatrix}.$$

d. Explain why

$$\begin{bmatrix} 18 & 0 & 0 \\ 0 & 4 & 0 \end{bmatrix} V^T = \begin{bmatrix} 18 & 0 \\ 0 & 4 \end{bmatrix} \begin{bmatrix} \mathbf{v}_1 & \mathbf{v}_2 \end{bmatrix}^T.$$

e. If $A = U\Sigma V^T$, explain why $A = U_r\Sigma_r V_r^T$ where the columns of U_r are an orthonormal basis for $\text{Col}(A)$, Σ_r is a square, diagonal, invertible matrix, and the columns of V_r form an orthonormal basis for $\text{Col}(A^T)$.

7.5 Using Singular Value Decompositions

Preview Activity 7.5.1 Suppose that $A = U\Sigma V^T$ where

$$\Sigma = \begin{bmatrix} 13 & 0 & 0 & 0 \\ 0 & 8 & 0 & 0 \\ 0 & 0 & 2 & 0 \\ 0 & 0 & 0 & 0 \\ 0 & 0 & 0 & 0 \end{bmatrix},$$

vectors $\mathbf{u}_j$ form the columns of U, and vectors $\mathbf{v}_j$ form the columns of V.

a. What are the shapes of the matrices A, U, and V?

b. What is the rank of A?

c. Describe how to find an orthonormal basis for Col(A).

d. Describe how to find an orthonormal basis for Nul(A).

e. If the columns of Q form an orthonormal basis for Col(A), what is Q^TQ?

f. How would you form a matrix that projects vectors orthogonally onto Col(A)?

Activity 7.5.2 Consider the equation $A\mathbf{x} = \mathbf{b}$ where

$$\begin{bmatrix} 1 & 0 \\ 1 & 1 \\ 1 & 2 \end{bmatrix} \mathbf{x} = \begin{bmatrix} -1 \\ 3 \\ 6 \end{bmatrix}$$

a. Find a singular value decomposition for A using the Sage cell below. What are singular values of A?

b. What is r, the rank of A? How can we identify an orthonormal basis for Col(A)?

c. Form the reduced singular value decomposition $U_r\Sigma_r V_r^T$ by constructing: the matrix U_r, consisting of the first r columns of U; the matrix V_r, consisting of the first r columns of V; and Σ_r, a square $r \times r$ diagonal matrix. Verify that $A = U_r\Sigma_r V_r^T$.

   You may find it convenient to remember that if `B` is a matrix defined in Sage, then `B.matrix_from_columns( list )` and `B.matrix_from_rows( list )` can be used to extract columns or rows from `B`. For instance, you may use `B.matrix_from_rows([0,1,2])` to obtain a matrix formed from the first three rows of `B`.

d. How does the reduced singular value decomposition provide a matrix whose columns are an orthonormal basis for Col(A)?

e. Explain why a least-squares approximate solution $\widehat{\mathbf{x}}$ satisfies

$$A\widehat{\mathbf{x}} = U_r U_r^T \mathbf{b}.$$

f. What is the product $V_r^T V_r$ and why does it have this form?

g. Explain why

$$\widehat{\mathbf{x}} = V_r \Sigma_r^{-1} U_r^T \mathbf{b}$$

   is the least-squares approximate solution, and use this expression to find $\widehat{\mathbf{x}}$.

Activity 7.5.3 Let's consider a matrix $A = U\Sigma V^T$ where

$$U = \begin{bmatrix} \frac{1}{2} & \frac{1}{2} & \frac{1}{2} & \frac{1}{2} \\ \frac{1}{2} & \frac{1}{2} & -\frac{1}{2} & -\frac{1}{2} \\ \frac{1}{2} & -\frac{1}{2} & \frac{1}{2} & -\frac{1}{2} \\ \frac{1}{2} & -\frac{1}{2} & -\frac{1}{2} & \frac{1}{2} \end{bmatrix}, \quad \Sigma = \begin{bmatrix} 500 & 0 & 0 & 0 \\ 0 & 100 & 0 & 0 \\ 0 & 0 & 20 & 0 \\ 0 & 0 & 0 & 4 \end{bmatrix}$$

$$V = \begin{bmatrix} \frac{1}{2} & \frac{1}{2} & \frac{1}{2} & \frac{1}{2} \\ \frac{1}{2} & -\frac{1}{2} & -\frac{1}{2} & \frac{1}{2} \\ -\frac{1}{2} & -\frac{1}{2} & \frac{1}{2} & \frac{1}{2} \\ -\frac{1}{2} & \frac{1}{2} & -\frac{1}{2} & \frac{1}{2} \end{bmatrix}$$

Evaluating the following cell will create the matrices `U`, `V`, and `Sigma`. Notice how the `diagonal_matrix` command provides a convenient way to form the diagonal matrix Σ.

```
h = 1/2
U = matrix(4,4,[h,h,h,h,  h,h,-h,-h,  h,-h,h,-h,  h,-h,-h,h])
V = matrix(4,4,[h,h,h,h,  h,-h,-h,h,  -h,-h,h,h,  -h,h,-h,h])
Sigma = diagonal_matrix([500, 100, 20, 4])
```

a. Form the matrix $A = U\Sigma V^T$. What is $\text{rank}(A)$?

b. Now form the approximating matrix $A_1 = U\Sigma^{(1)}V^T$. What is $\text{rank}(A_1)$?

c. Find the error in the approximation $A \approx A_1$ by finding $A - A_1$.

d. Now find $A_2 = U\Sigma^{(2)}V^T$ and the error $A - A_2$. What is $\text{rank}(A_2)$?

e. Find $A_3 = U\Sigma^{(3)}V^T$ and the error $A - A_3$. What is $\text{rank}(A_3)$?

f. What would happen if we were to compute A_4?

g. What do you notice about the error $A - A_k$ as k increases?

Activity 7.5.4 Let's revisit the iris data set that we studied in Section 7.3. Remember that there are four measurements given for each of 150 irises and that each iris belongs to one of three species.

Evaluating the following cell will load the dataset and define the demeaned data matrix A whose shape is 4×150.

```
url='https://raw.githubusercontent.com/davidaustinm/'
url+='ula_modules/master/pca_iris.py'
sage.repl.load.load(url, globals())
df.T
```

a. Find the singular values of A using the command `A.singular_values()` and use them to determine the variance $V_{\mathbf{u}_j}$ in the direction of each of the four principal components. What is the fraction of variance retained by the first two principal components?

b. We will now write the matrix $\Gamma = \Sigma V^T$ so that $A = U\Gamma$. Suppose that a demeaned data point, say, the 100th column of A, is written as a linear combination of principal components:

$$\mathbf{x} = c_1\mathbf{u}_1 + c_2\mathbf{u}_2 + c_3\mathbf{u}_3 + c_4\mathbf{u}_4.$$

Explain why $\begin{bmatrix} c_1 \\ c_2 \\ c_3 \\ c_4 \end{bmatrix}$, the vector of coordinates of $\mathbf{x}$ in the basis of principal components, appears as 100th column of Γ.

c. Suppose that we now project this demeaned data point $\mathbf{x}$ orthogonally onto the subspace spanned by the first two principal components $\mathbf{u}_1$ and $\mathbf{u}_2$. What are the coordinates of the projected point in this basis and how can we find them in the matrix Γ?

d. Alternatively, consider the approximation $A_2 = U_2\Sigma_2V_2^T$ of the demeaned data matrix A. Explain why the 100th column of A_2 represents the projection of $\mathbf{x}$ onto the two-dimensional subspace spanned by the first two principal components, $\mathbf{u}_1$ and $\mathbf{u}_2$. Then explain why the coefficients in that projection, $c_1\mathbf{u}_1 + c_2\mathbf{u}_2$, form the two-dimensional vector $\begin{bmatrix} c_1 \\ c_2 \end{bmatrix}$ that is the 100th column of $\Gamma_2 = \Sigma_2 V_2^T$.

e. Now we've seen that the columns of $\Gamma_2 = \Sigma_2 V_2^T$ form the coordinates of the demeaned data points projected on to the two-dimensional subspace spanned by $\mathbf{u}_1$ and $\mathbf{u}_2$. In the cell below, find a singular value decomposition of A and use it to form the matrix `Gamma2`. When you evaluate this cell, you will see a plot of the projected demeaned data plots, similar to the one we created in Section 7.3.

```
# Form the SVD of A and use it to form Gamma2


Gamma2 =

# The following will plot the projected demeaned data points
data = Gamma2.columns()
(list_plot(data[:50], color='blue', aspect_ratio=1) +
 list_plot(data[50:100], color='orange') +
 list_plot(data[100:], color='green'))
```

Activity 7.5.5 Evaluating the following cell loads some data that we'll use in this activity. To begin, it defines and displays a 25×15 matrix A.

```
url='https://raw.githubusercontent.com/davidaustinm/'
url+='ula_modules/master/svd_compress.py'
sage.repl.load.load(url, globals())
print(A)
```

a. If we interpret 0 as black and 1 as white, this matrix represents an image as shown below.

```
display_matrix(A)
```

We will explore how the singular value decomposition helps us to compress this image.

1. By inspecting the image represented by A, identify a basis for Col(A) and determine rank(A).
2. The following cell plots the singular values of A. Explain how this plot verifies that the rank is what you found in the previous part.

```
plot_sv(A)
```

3. There is a command `approximate(A, k)` that creates the approximation A_k. Use the cell below to define k and look at the images represented by the first few approximations. What is the smallest value of k for which $A = A_k$?

```
k =
display_matrix(approximate(A, k))
```

4. Now we can see how the singular value decomposition allows us to compress images. Since this is a 25×15 matrix, we need $25 \cdot 15 = 375$ numbers to represent the image. However, we can also reconstruct the image using a small number of singular values and vectors:

$$A = A_k = \sigma_1 \mathbf{u}_1 \mathbf{v}_1^T + \sigma_2 \mathbf{u}_2 \mathbf{v}_2^T + \ldots + \sigma_k \mathbf{u}_k \mathbf{v}_k^T.$$

What are the dimensions of the singular vectors $\mathbf{u}_i$ and $\mathbf{v}_i$? Between the singular vectors and singular values, how many numbers do we need to reconstruct A_k for the smallest k for which $A = A_k$? This is the compressed size of the image.

5. The *compression ratio* is the ratio of the uncompressed size to the compressed size. What compression ratio does this represent?

b. Next we'll explore an example based on a photograph.

1. Consider the following image consisting of an array of 316×310 pixels stored in the matrix A.

```
A = matrix(RDF, image)
display_image(A)
```

Plot the singular values of A.

```
plot_sv(A)
```

2. Use the cell below to study the approximations A_k for $k = 1, 10, 20, 50, 100$.

```
k = 1
display_image(approximate(A, k))
```

Notice how the approximating image A_k more closely approximates the original image A as k increases. What is the compression ratio when $k = 50$? What is the compression ratio when $k = 100$? Notice how a higher compression ratio leads to a lower quality reconstruction of the image.

c. A second, related application of the singular value decomposition to image processing is called *denoising*. For example, consider the image represented by the matrix A below.

```
A = matrix(RDF, noise.values)
display_matrix(A)
```

This image is similar to the image of the letter "O" we first studied in this activity, but there are splotchy regions in the background that result, perhaps, from scanning the image. We think of the splotchy regions as noise, and our goal is to improve the quality of the image by reducing the noise.

1. Plot the singular values below. How are the singular values of this matrix similar to those represented by the clean image that we considered earlier and how are they different?

```
plot_sv(A)
```

2. There is a natural point where the singular values dramatically decrease so it makes sense to think of the noise as being formed by the small singular values. To denoise the image, we will therefore replace A by its approximation A_k, where k is the point at which the singular values drop off. This has the effect of setting the small singular values to zero and hence eliminating the noise. Choose an appropriate value of k below and notice that the new image appears to be somewhat cleaned up as a result of removing the noise.

```
k =
display_matrix(approximate(A, k))
```

Activity 7.5.6 Evaluating the following cell loads and displays a dataset describing the votes of each justice in these 911 cases. More specifically, an entry of +1 means that the justice represented by the row voted with the majority in the case represented by the column. An entry of -1 means that justice was in the minority. This information is also stored in the 9×911 matrix A.

```
url='https://raw.githubusercontent.com/davidaustinm/'
url+='ula_modules/master/svd_supreme.py'
sage.repl.load.load(url, globals())
A = matrix(RDF, cases.values)
cases
```

The justices are listed, very roughly, in order from more conservative to more progressive.

In this activity, it will be helpful to visualize the entries in various matrices and vectors. The next cell displays the first 50 columns of the matrix A with white representing an entry of +1, red representing -1, and black representing 0.

```
display_matrix(A.matrix_from_columns(range(50)))
```

a. Plot the singular values of A below. Describe the significance of this plot, including the relative contributions from the singular values σ_k as k increases.

```
plot_sv(A)
```

b. Form the singular value decomposition $A = U\Sigma V^T$ and the matrix of coefficients Γ so that $A = U\Gamma$.

c. We will now study a particular case, the second case which appears as the column of A indexed by `1`. There is a command `display_column(A, k)` that provides a visual display of the kth column of a matrix A. Describe the justices' votes in the second case.

d. Also, display the first left singular vector $\mathbf{u}_1$, the column of U indexed by 0, and the column of Γ holding the coefficients that express the second case as a linear combination of left singular vectors.

What does this tell us about how the second case is constructed as a linear combination of left singular vectors? What is the significance of the first left singular vector $\mathbf{u}_1$?

e. Let's now study the 48th case, which is represented by the column of A indexed by `47`. Describe the voting pattern in this case.

f. Display the second left singular vector $\mathbf{u}_2$ and the vector of coefficients that express the 48th case as a linear combination of left singular vectors.

Describe how this case is constructed as a linear combination of singular vectors. What is the significance of the second left singular vector $\mathbf{u}_2$?

g. The data in Table 7.5.2 describes the number of cases decided by each possible vote count.

Table 7.5.2 Number of cases by vote count

Vote count	# of cases
9-0	405
8-1	89
7-2	111
6-3	118
5-4	188

How do the singular vectors $\mathbf{u}_1$ and $\mathbf{u}_2$ reflect this data? Would you characterize the court as leaning toward the conservatives or progressives? Use these singular vectors to explain your response.

h. Cases decided by a 5-4 vote are often the most impactful as they represent a sharp divide among the justices and, often, society at large. For that reason, we will now focus on the 5-4 decisions. Evaluating the next cell forms the 9×188 matrix B consisting of 5-4 decisions.

```
B = matrix(RDF, fivefour.values)
display_matrix(B.matrix_from_columns(range(50)))
```

Form the singular value decomposition of $B = U\Sigma V^T$ along with the matrix Γ of coefficients so that $B = U\Gamma$ and display the first left singular vector $\mathbf{u}_1$. Study how the 7th case, indexed by `6`, is constructed as a linear combination of left singular vectors.

```
```

What does this singular vector tell us about the make up of the court and whether it leans towards the conservatives or progressives?

i. Display the second left singular vector $\mathbf{u}_2$ and study how the 6th case, indexed by `5`, is constructed as a linear combination of left singular vectors.

```
```

What does $\mathbf{u}_2$ tell us about the relative importance of the justices' voting records?

j. By a *swing vote*, we mean a justice who is less inclined to vote with a particular bloc of justices but instead swings from one bloc to another with the potential to sway close decisions. What do the singular vectors $\mathbf{u}_1$ and $\mathbf{u}_2$ tell us about the presence of voting blocs on the court and the presence of a swing vote? Which justice represents the swing vote?